Letts
and
LONSDALE

GCSE
Success

Workbook

Additional
Science
Higher

Brian Arnold • Elaine Gill • Emma Poole

Contents

Physics

Cells

A

1 **What are the building blocks of life?** (1 mark)

a) cells ☐
b) tissues ☐
c) organs ☐
d) systems ☐

2 **Which structure contains chlorophyll?** (1 mark)

a) chloroplasts ☑
b) cytoplasm ☐
c) cell wall ☐
d) nucleus ☐

3 **During which stage of human growth is there a growth spurt?** (1 mark)

a) infancy ☐
b) puberty ☑
c) maturity ☐
d) old age ☐

4 **Which part of a baby in the womb is largest at the beginning?** (1 mark)

a) arms ☐
b) body ☐
c) head ☐
d) legs ☐

5 **Which cells have lots of chloroplasts?** (1 mark)

a) ciliated ☐
b) nerve ☐
c) palisade ☑
d) xylem ☐

B

1 **The diagram shows an animal cell.**

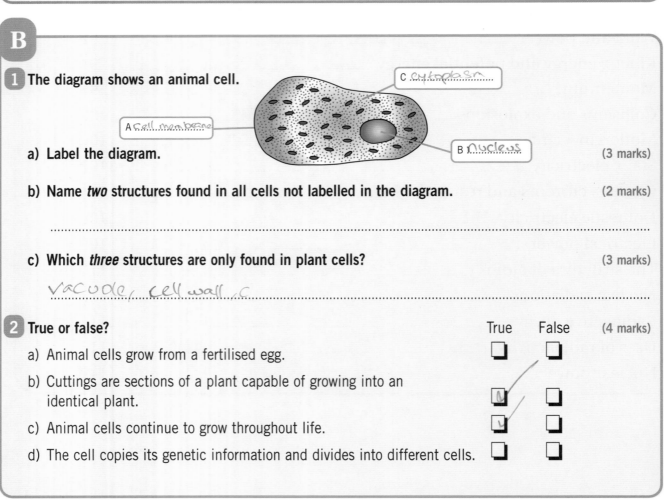

C cytoplasm

A cell membrane

B nucleus

a) Label the diagram. (3 marks)

b) Name *two* structures found in all cells not labelled in the diagram. (2 marks)

....

c) Which *three* structures are only found in plant cells? (3 marks)

vacuole, cell wall, c

2 **True or false?** True False (4 marks)

a) Animal cells grow from a fertilised egg. ☐ ☐

b) Cuttings are sections of a plant capable of growing into an identical plant. ☑ ☐

c) Animal cells continue to grow throughout life. ☑ ☐

d) The cell copies its genetic information and divides into different cells. ☐ ☐

C

1 Join the boxes with straight lines to show the function of each structure. (7 marks)

Structure	Function (job)
Cytoplasm	Contains a weak solution of salt and sugar called cell sap and gives the cell support
Cell membrane	They absorb the Sun's energy so that the plant can make its own food
Mitochondria	This controls all the chemical reactions that take place inside the cell. It also contains all the information needed to produce a new living organism
Nucleus	Made of cellulose, which gives a plant cell strength and support
Cell wall	This is where the chemical reactions take place
Chloroplasts	Where respiration takes place
Vacuole	This controls what passes in and out of the cell

2 The diagrams show some cells that have been specialised to carry out a specific function (job).

Name each type of cell, say how it is specialised and what function it performs. (9 marks)

A   B   C

A .... Sperm cell ....

B .. Blood cells ....

C ....

3 Cells make animals and plants.

Complete the flow diagram to show the order they are put together. Use these words: (4 marks)

cells   organisms   organs   systems   tissues

Systems → cells → tisues → orgens → organisos

4 This question is about multi-cellular and unicellular organisms.

a) What does multi-cellular mean? (1 mark)

....

b) What advantage does a multi-cellular organism have? (3 marks)

....

c) Give an example of a unicellular organism. (1 mark)

....

d) How does a unicellular organism get the oxygen and food it needs? (1 mark)

....

How well did you do?   0-17 Try again   18-26 Getting there   27-34 Good work   35-43 Excellent!

5

Diffusion and osmosis

A

1 **Which structure is partially permeable?** (1 mark)

a) cell wall ☐
b) cell membrane ☐
c) nucleus ☐
d) cytoplasm ☐

2 **When a plant cell is full of water it is:** (1 mark)

a) flaccid ☐
b) concentrated ☐
c) plasmolysed ☐
d) turgid ☐

3 **What does the net movement of water mean?** (1 mark)

a) water moves more one way ☐
b) water moves both ways equally ☐
c) water moves in circles ☐
d) water does not move ☐

4 **What structures are on the underside of a leaf?** (1 mark)

a) palisade cell ☐
b) stomata ☐
c) spongy cells ☐
d) xylem ☐

5 **Which substance moves by osmosis?** (1 mark)

a) sugar ☐
b) salt ☐
c) alcohol ☐
d) water ☐

B

1 **The diagram shows a cell and a capillary in the human body.**

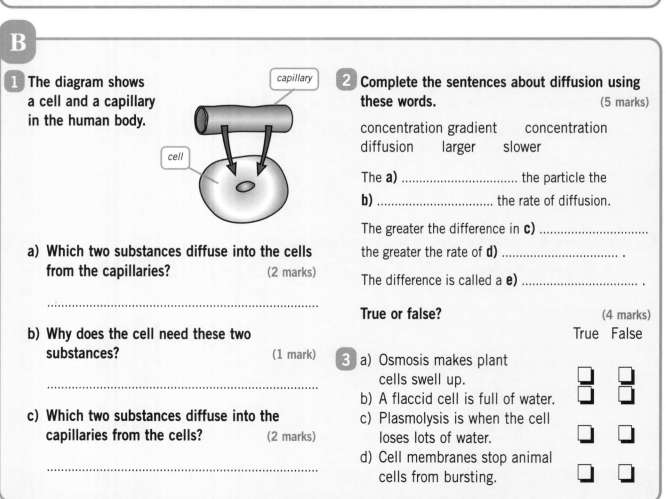

capillary

cell

a) Which two substances diffuse into the cells from the capillaries? (2 marks)

....

b) Why does the cell need these two substances? (1 mark)

....

c) Which two substances diffuse into the capillaries from the cells? (2 marks)

....

2 **Complete the sentences about diffusion using these words.** (5 marks)

concentration gradient   concentration
diffusion   larger   slower

The **a)** .... the particle the

b) .... the rate of diffusion.

The greater the difference in **c)** ....

the greater the rate of **d)** ....

The difference is called a **e)** ....

True or false? (4 marks)

	True	False
3 a) Osmosis makes plant cells swell up.	☐	☐
b) A flaccid cell is full of water.	☐	☐
c) Plasmolysis is when the cell loses lots of water.	☐	☐
d) Cell membranes stop animal cells from bursting.	☐	☐

C

1 The diagram shows a cross-section of a leaf.

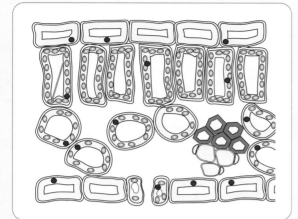

a) Carbon dioxide is needed for photosynthesis. Draw an arrow labelled A on the diagram to show how this gas gets into the leaf. (1 mark)

b) Write down two gases that leave the leaf. (2 marks)

Oxygen and

c) Name the process by which gases enter and leave the leaf. (1 mark)

d) What would be the best conditions for drying clothes on a line? (3 marks)

2 The diagram shows a plant cell before and after being placed into a concentrated sugar solution.

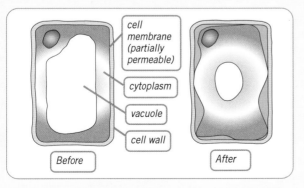

cell membrane (partially permeable)

cytoplasm

vacuole

cell wall

Before

After

a) What has happened to the size of the vacuole? (1 mark)

it has decreased

b) Explain why the size of the vacuole has changed. (4 marks)

c) Give an example of where osmosis occurs in plants. (1 mark)

3 a) Complete these sentences. (9 marks)

Water is absorbed from the **i)** roots by **ii)** .... on the root. The water and **iii)** nutrients are transported by **iv)** the stem .

The movement and eventual loss of **v)** .... through the plant is called the transpiration stream.

The transpiration stream provides the plant with water for **vi)** .... , photosynthesis, **vii)** .... and the movement of minerals (dissolved in water).

The water ends in the leaves where it is lost by **viii)** .... through the **ix)** ....

b) State three factors that affect the rate of transpiration. (3 marks)

c) Which cells control the opening and closing of the stomata? (1 mark)

How well did you do?   0-18 Try again   19-27 Getting there   28-36 Good work   37-45 Excellent!

Photosynthesis

A

1 **Which gas enters the leaf through tiny holes in the bottom surface of the leaf?** (1 mark)

a) carbon dioxide
b) oxygen
c) hydrogen
d) nitrogen

2 **When is the rate of photosynthesis at its highest in Britain?** (1 mark)

a) spring
b) summer
c) autumn
d) winter

3 **Which layer allows gases to circulate?** (1 mark)

a) upper epidermis
b) palisade
c) spongy
d) lower epidermis

4 **Which substance is needed for photosynthesis?** (1 mark)

a) chlorophyll
b) oxygen
c) hydrogen
d) glucose

5 **What is the green pigment in plants called?** (1 mark)

a) chloroform
b) chlorophyll
c) chloroplasts
d) cellulose

B

1 **a) Write down the chemical equation for photosynthesis.** (2 marks)

CO2 + H2o + light energy - glucose + oxygen

b) Write down the three factors that affect the rate of photosynthesis. (3 marks)

....

2 **a) What happens to the oxygen produced?** (2 marks)

....

b) How do plants increase their biomass? (2 marks)

....

c) Write down three ways in which the biomass of plants can be used. (3 marks)

....

3 **Plants can be selectively bred or genetically modified.**

Why are these techniques beneficial? (2 marks)

....
....

4 **There are four essential minerals needed for healthy growth.**

Complete the sentences to show which nutrient is needed. Chose your answer from this list:

magnesium   nitrates   phosphates   potassium

a) .... **are needed for making proteins.** (1 mark)

b) .... **play an important role in growth.** (1 mark)

c) .... **is involved in making the enzymes used in respiration work.** (1 mark)

d) .... **is needed in small amounts to make chlorophyll.** (1 mark)

C

1 The diagram shows a section through a leaf.

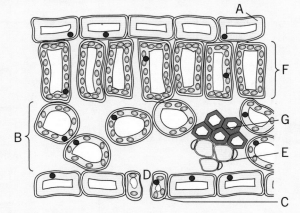

a) Name the following structures. (4 marks)

B ....

D ....

C ....

F ....

b) i) Where does most photosynthesis take place? (1 mark)

....

ii) Where do gases enter and leave the leaf? (1 mark)

....

iii) Which of the structures contains most chloroplasts? (1 mark)

....

iv) Which two structures make up the vein? (1 mark)

....

....

2 The graph shows the effect of increasing temperature on the rate of photosynthesis.

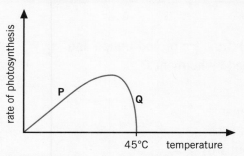

a) Explain what is happening at P. (2 marks)

....

....

b) Explain what is happening at Q. (3 marks)

....

....

....

c) In Britain why is the rate of photosynthesis low? (1 mark)

....

d) In winter how do commercial growers of plants increase the rate of photosynthesis? (1 mark)

....

3 Complete the sentences. (5 marks)

Chloroplasts are most abundant in

a) .... cells. These cells are near

the b) .... surface of the leaf.

Chloroplasts contain the pigment

c) .... Chlorophyll is a

d) .... pigment that absorbs

e) .... energy.

Plant hormones

A

1 Which fruit are picked unripe and ripened by hormones? *(1 mark)*

a) apples ☐
b) bananas ☐
c) oranges ☐
d) rhubarb ☐

2 Which plants are not affected by weedkillers? *(1 mark)*

a) dandelions ☐
b) cereals ☐
c) daisies ☐
d) roses ☐

3 Where does plant growth mainly take place? *(1 mark)*

a) leaf ☐
b) flower ☐
c) shoot tip ☐
d) root hair ☐

4 Where are hormones found in a plant? *(1 mark)*

a) leaf ☐
b) flower ☐
c) shoot tip ☐
d) root hair ☐

5 What effect does auxin have on root cells? *(1 mark)*

a) makes them grow bigger ☐
b) makes them grow faster ☐
c) makes them grow slower ☐
d) stops them growing ☐

B

1 Plants respond to environmental stimuli.

a) What is the response to these stimuli called?

i) gravity *(1 mark)*

....

ii) light *(1 mark)*

....

b) Name the chemical responsible for the responses. *(1 mark)*

....

2 A plant is growing in a room with a window at one side only.

Sun

a) Draw another plant to show how the plant will look after 3 days. *(1 mark)*

b) Why does the plant grow in this way? *(2 marks)*

....

....

c) Where does the auxin accumulate in the shoot when the light is on one side? *(1 mark)*

....

d) Where does the auxin accumulate in the shoot when the light is all round the plant? *(1 mark)*

....

C

1 The diagram shows a seed that was planted upside down.

a) On the diagram, draw and label where the shoot and root would grow. (2 marks)

b) Explain why you have drawn the shoot and root in this way. (2 marks)

....

....

2 Another seed which had already started to grow was placed on its side.

The root and shoot continue to grow.

a) On the diagram, shade where the auxin would collect in the root and shoot. (2 marks)

b) On the diagram, draw the root and shoot as they would look after 7 days. (2 marks)

c) Describe the effect auxin has on

   i) the root (2 marks)

   ....

   ....

   ii) the shoot (2 marks)

   ....

   ....

3 Rooting powder contains synthetic hormones.

How do gardeners use rooting powder? (3 marks)

....

....

....

4 a) How are auxins used as selective weedkillers? (2 marks)

   ....

   ....

   b) How are seedless grapes produced? (3 marks)

   ....

   ....

   ....

   c) Describe one other way that synthetic hormones are used. (1 mark)

   ....

How well did you do?   ✗ 0-14 Try again   15-20 Getting there   21-27 Good work   28-34 Excellent! ✓

Pyramids of numbers and biomass

A

1 **What does a pyramid of numbers tell us?** (1 mark)

a) animals that live together
b) number of organisms in a food chain
c) organisms that are similar
d) where organisms live

2 **Why do food chains rarely have more than four or five links in them?** (1 mark)

a) animals at the beginning are too big
b) energy is lost
c) producers cannot make enough food
d) too many plants die

3 **What is the name for a level in a food chain?** (1 mark)

a) first level
b) floor level
c) plant level
d) trophic level

4 **What does a pyramid of biomass tell us?** (1 mark)

a) animals that live together
b) mass of organism in a food chain
c) organisms that are different
d) who eats who

5 **What sort of energy is mainly released during respiration to the surroundings?** (1 mark)

a) heat
b) light
c) movement
d) sound

B

1 **Here is a food chain.** grass → rabbit → owl

a) **What does the rabbit eat?** .... (1 mark)

b) **In this chain there were 1000 grass plants, 10 rabbits and 1 owl.**

Draw a pyramid of numbers for this food chain. (3 marks)

c) **Another chain had 1 rose bush, 1000 greenfly and 10 ladybirds.**

Draw a pyramid of numbers for this food chain. (3 marks)

d) **Why is a pyramid of numbers misleading?** .... (1 mark)

2 **Complete these sentences.**

a) **Plants obtain their energy from the** .... (1 mark)

b) **Energy is used when glucose is made during** .... (1 mark)

c) **Plants make their food and are called** .... (1 mark)

d) **Animals that eat plants are called** .... (1 mark)

e) **When plants shed their leaves, they are eaten by** .... (1 mark)

C

1 Here is a pyramid of numbers.

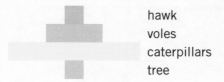

hawk
voles
caterpillars
tree

a) Draw a pyramid of biomass for this food chain. *(1 mark)*

b) Biomass is calculated by multiplying the number of organisms by the mass of one organism. If there are 2000 caterpillars each having a mass of 2 grams, calculate the biomass of caterpillars. *(2 marks)*

....

....

c) What would you expect the biomass of hawks to be? Underline your answer. *(1 mark)*

greater   lower   same

d) What would you expect the biomass of the tree to be? Underline your answer. *(1 mark)*

greater   lower   same

2 Complete these sentences.

a) Only 10% of the original energy from the sun is passed to the .... *(1 mark)*

b) 90% of the energy losses are in the life processes of
.... and .... *(2 marks)*

3 The diagram shows a sheep and its energy gains and losses.

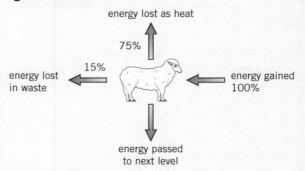

energy lost as heat

75%

energy lost in waste   15%   energy gained 100%

energy passed to next level

a) Calculate how much energy is passed on to the next level. *(2 marks)*

....

....

b) How is most energy lost from this sheep? *(1 mark)*

....

c) Suggest what form the waste might take. *(2 marks)*

....

d) How is energy gained? *(1 mark)*

....

4 a) How would you calculate the efficiency of energy transfer? *(2 marks)*

....

....

b) If 1000 joules of energy entered the food chain and 100 joules was passed to the primary consumer, calculate the efficiency of energy transfer. *(2 marks)*

....

....

The carbon cycle

A

1 What is the percentage of the air made up of carbon dioxide? (1 mark)

a) 0.03
b) 0.3
c) 3.0
d) 30

2 What should happen to the amount of carbon dioxide in the air? (1 mark)

a) increase
b) decrease
c) remain constant
d) double each month

3 What do bacteria and fungi in the soil break down? (1 mark)

a) water
b) dead matter
c) soil particles
d) air

4 What happens in a compost heap? (1 mark)

a) fossilisation
b) decomposition
c) transpiration
d) photosynthesis

5 What does compost, when rotted down, contain? (1 mark)

a) fossil fuel
b) dead plants
c) nutrients
d) rocks

B

1 Photosynthesis takes place during the carbon cycle.

a) Which gas is a raw material? .... (1 mark)

b) What is the carbon turned into? .... (3 marks)

c) Where does the energy come from? .... (1 mark)

2 Respiration takes place during the carbon cycle.

a) Which gas is returned to the air? .... (1 mark)

b) Which three groups of organisms carry out respiration as part of the carbon cycle? (3 marks)

....

3 a) What are animals that feed on dead and decaying matter called? (1 mark)

....

b) What part do they play in the carbon cycle? .... (1 mark)

c) Name three detritovores. .... (3 marks)

14

C

1 The diagram shows the carbon cycle.

a) Name the processes A–F. (6 marks)

A ....

B ....

C ....

D ....

E ....

F ....

b) Carbon is in the air. In which compound is it found? (1 mark)

....

c) Name three fossil fuels. (3 marks)

....

....

....

d) Carbon is returned to the air from dead plants and animals by decomposition.

Which organisms help in this? (2 marks)

....

....

e) Name three things needed for decay. (3 marks)

....

....

2 Explain how dead plants and animals are turned into fossil fuels. (3 marks)

....

....

....

3 Other non-natural substances can be recycled.

a) Why is the recycling of these substances important? (2 marks)

....

....

b) Why is it important to recycle plastics? (2 marks)

....

....

c) Which metal can be recycled? (1 mark)

....

d) Name one other substance that can be recycled. (1 mark)

....

4 a) What is a saprophyte? (1 mark)

....

b) Name two saprophytes. (2 marks)

....

....

How well did you do? ✗ 0-18 **Try again**   19-28 **Getting there**   29-37 **Good work**   38-46 **Excellent!** ✓

15

The nitrogen cycle

A

1 What percentage of the air is nitrogen? (1 mark)

- a) 70 ☐
- b) 78 ☐
- c) 80 ☑
- d) 87 ☐

2 What can be added to the soil to improve the nitrate content? (1 mark)

- a) peat ☐
- b) fertilisers ☐
- c) insecticides ☐
- d) pesticides ☐

3 Which organisms are detritovores? (1 mark)

- a) bacteria ☐
- b) fungi ☐
- c) maggots ☐
- d) viruses ☐

4 What is washing nitrates out of the soil before it can be used called? (1 mark)

- a) eutrophication ☐
- b) denitrification ☐
- c) leaching ☐
- d) nitrification ☐

5 Which weather condition plays a part in the nitrogen cycle? (1 mark)

- a) lightning ☐
- b) rain ☐
- c) snow ☐
- d) thunder ☐

B

1 a) Explain the role of detritovores in the nitrogen cycle. (2 marks)

....

b) Write down three things that detritovores eat. (3 marks)

....

c) Name two decomposers. (2 marks)

....

d) What is the job of the decomposers? (1 mark)

....

2 a) What happens to the nitrates in the soil? (2 marks)

....

b) What happens to the protein in the plants? (3 marks)

....

C

1 The diagram represents the nitrogen cycle.

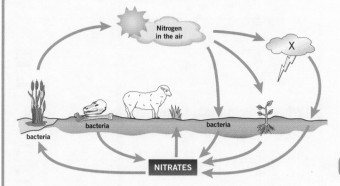

a) On the diagram, write the following letters in the places described.

i) A in two places where nitrogen-fixing bacteria are found.   (2 marks)

ii) B in one place where nitrifying bacteria are found.   (1 mark)

iii) C in one place where denitrifying bacteria are found.   (1 mark)

b) On the diagram, write the letter:

i) P in three places where nitrogen is changed into nitrates.   (3 marks)

ii) Q in one place where protein is changed into nitrates.   (1 mark)

iii) R in one place where nitrates are changed into nitrogen.   (1 mark)

c) How does the plant protein become animal protein?   (2 marks)

....

d) What is leaching?   (2 marks)

....

e) Name three plants which have root nodules.   (3 marks)

....

f) i) What does X represent on the diagram?
            (1 mark)

....

ii) Describe the part it plays in the nitrogen cycle.   (3 marks)

....

2 Bacteria are used in the nitrogen cycle.

a) What is the job of the following?

i)   nitrogen-fixing bacteria   (2 marks)

....

....

ii) denitrifying bacteria   (3 marks)

....

....

....

iii) nitrifying bacteria   (2 marks)

....

....

b) Where are denitrifying bacteria found?
            (1 mark)

....

c) Where do you find nitrogen-fixing bacteria?   (3 marks)

....

....

....

Enzymes and digestion

A

1 Which enzymes are used in slimming foods? *(1 mark)*

a) carbohydrases
b) isomerases
c) lipases
d) proteases

2 What does catalysed mean? *(1 mark)*

a) left alone
b) broken down
c) slowed down
d) speeded up

3 What is digested food absorbed into? *(1 mark)*

a) blood ✓
b) brain
c) heart
d) kidney

4 What are catalysts called in the digestive system? *(1 mark)*

a) antigens
b) antibodies
c) enzymes
d) hormones

5 What are enzymes made of? *(1 mark)*

a) amino acids ✓
b) fatty acids
c) glucose
d) glycerol

B

1 a) Complete these sentences using words from this list. *(8 marks)*

active site   catalysts   denatured   pH   photosynthesis   respiration   temperature   optimum

Enzymes are biological **i)** .... They speed up biological reactions inside body cells such as **ii)** .... , protein synthesis and **iii)** .... Enzyme activity is affected by **iv)** .... and **v)** .... and each enzyme has its own **vi)** .... conditions. At too low temperatures the rate at which the substrate joins with the enzyme's **vii)** .... is slowed down so the reaction is slower. At too high temperatures or extremes of pH the enzyme becomes **viii)** .... This means the active site is distorted and the reaction no longer occurs.

b) How do the enzyme and substrate fit together? Underline the correct answer. *(1 mark)*

hammer and nail   lock and key   nut and bolt

2 Write down two reasons why enzymes are used in industry and the home. *(2 marks)*

....

3 Complete these sentences.

a) Long chains of amino acids make .... *(1 mark)*

b) Enzymes are folded into a specific .... *(1 mark)*

c) Molecules that fit into an enzyme are called .... *(1 mark)*

d) The place where molecules fit into an enzyme is called an .... *(1 mark)*

C

1 Join the boxes using straight lines to show where each food is digested and what the end product is. (6 marks)

Food	Where digested	End product
Starch	Stomach and small intestine	Fatty acids and glycerol
Protein	Mouth and small intestine	Amino acids
Fats	Small intestine	Glucose

2 Complete the passage by using these words. (4 marks)

diffusion   enzymes   large insoluble   small soluble

Digestion is the breaking down of
a) ...*large* ...*small soluble*... molecules into
b) ...*large insoluble*... molecules so that they can be absorbed into the blood stream by
c) ...*enzymes*... . The large insoluble molecules are starch, protein and fat. This action is speeded up (catalysed) by
d) ...*diffusion*... .

3 a) Name the two types of enzyme in biological washing powders. (2 marks)

....

b) What does each enzyme do? (2 marks)

....

....

c) How are proteases used in making baby food? (1 mark)

....

d) How are carbohydrases used in industry? (2 marks)

....

4 Write about the two types of physical digestion in the body. (4 marks)

....

5 Here is a diagram of the digestive system.

a) Label the mouth, oesophagus, stomach, pancreas, small and large intestine. (6 marks)

b) On the diagram, write letters to show where the following take place: (4 marks)

A – hydrochloric acid is produced
B – teeth start the breakdown of food
C – where food is absorbed into the blood
D – where faeces are stored

6 Explain why the liver is important in digestion. (4 marks)

....

....

7 Describe the functions of the stomach. (4 marks)

....

....

....

....

How well did you do?   0-24 Try again   25-35 Getting there   36-47 Good work   48-59 Excellent!

19

Respiration and exercise

A

1 Which gas is needed for aerobic respiration? (1 mark)

a) carbon dioxide ☐
b) hydrogen ☐
c) nitrogen ☐
d) oxygen ☐

2 Which of the statements is true about exercise? (1 mark)

a) the heart rate increases and the breathing rate increases ☐
b) the heart rate increases and the breathing rate decreases ☐
c) the heart rate decreases and the breathing rate increases ☐
d) the heart rate decreases and the breathing rate decreases ☐

3 Which gas is produced during respiration? (1 mark)

a) carbon dioxide ☐
b) hydrogen ☐
c) nitrogen ☐
d) oxygen ☐

4 What does aerobic mean? (1 mark)

a) with air (oxygen) ☐
b) with carbon dioxide ☐
c) without gas ☐
d) without water ☐

5 What do muscles need during exercise? (1 mark)

a) more carbon dioxide ☐
b) more oxygen + glucose ☐
c) less carbon dioxide ☐
d) less oxygen ☐

B

1 a) What is respiration? (1 mark)

....

b) Write down the chemical equation for respiration .... (2 marks)

c) Where in the cell does respiration take place? .... (1 mark)

d) Where and when in the body does respiration take place?................................... (2 marks)

e) What is the energy released in respiration used for? .... (1 mark)

2 Advice on exercise is changing all the time.

a) What is needed by most people to maintain good health? (1 mark)

....

b) What process provides the energy for exercise? (1 mark)

....

C

1 The graph shows the pulse rate of a fit person before, during and after exercise.

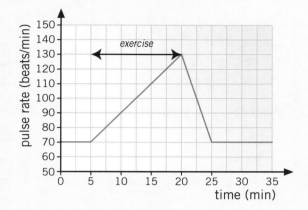

a) **What is the resting pulse rate?** (1 mark)

....

b) **By how much did the pulse rate increase during exercise?** (1 mark)

....

c) **How long after exercise did it return to the resting rate?** (1 mark)

....

d) **What is this time period called?** (1 mark)

....

e) **Draw on the graph the line you would expect for an unfit person.** (2 marks)

f) **What happens to the arteries during exercise and why?** (4 marks)

....

....

....

2 **Complete the sentences using these words.** (8 marks)

carbon dioxide	fitness	glucose
heart	muscles	normal
oxygen	recovery	

During exercise, respiration in the
a) .... increases.
Breathing and b) .... rate also increases, in order to deliver c) ....
and d) .... to the muscles more quickly and remove e) .... more quickly.
An increase in heart rate and breathing rate is
f) .... during exercise.
How much they increase during and after exercise can indicate a person's
g) .... One way of measuring fitness is to look at a person's
h) .... time after exercise.

3 a) **What is the aim of the Atkins diet?** (2 marks)

....

b) **List the health problems associated with the Atkins diet.** (4 marks)

....

....

4 **Breathing rate and pulse rate can be taken by hand. What is a more accurate way of taking these measurements? Explain why.** (3 marks)

....

....

5 **How is energy used in animals?** (6 marks)

....

....

....

Blood and blood vessels

A

1 **Which fluid transports food to cells?** *(1 mark)*

a) bile ☐
b) blood ☐
c) saliva ☐
d) urine ☐

2 **Which cell has a variable shape?** *(1 mark)*

a) all of them ☐
b) platelet ☐
c) red blood cell ☐
d) white blood cell ☐

3 **Which structure is only a cell fragment?**

(1 mark)

a) plasma ☐

b) platelet ☐
c) red blood cell ☐
d) white blood cell ☐

4 **What colour is plasma?** *(1 mark)*

a) blue ☐
b) green ☐
c) red ☐
d) yellow ☐

5 **What type of muscle is the heart made of?**

(1 mark)

a) cardiac ☐
b) coronary ☐
c) circulatory ☐
d) capillary ☐

B

1 **The diagram shows some of the components of blood.**

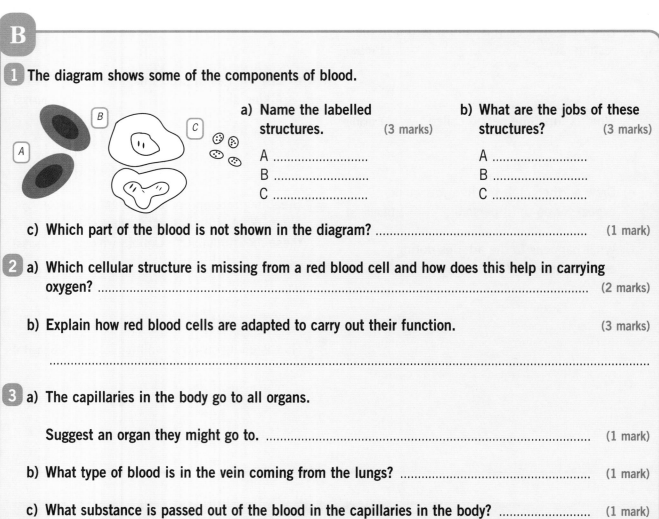

a) **Name the labelled structures.** *(3 marks)*

A ....
B ....
C ....

b) **What are the jobs of these structures?** *(3 marks)*

A ....
B ....
C ....

c) **Which part of the blood is not shown in the diagram?** .... *(1 mark)*

2 **a)** **Which cellular structure is missing from a red blood cell and how does this help in carrying oxygen?** .... *(2 marks)*

b) **Explain how red blood cells are adapted to carry out their function.** *(3 marks)*

....

3 **a)** **The capillaries in the body go to all organs.**

Suggest an organ they might go to. .... *(1 mark)*

b) **What type of blood is in the vein coming from the lungs?** .... *(1 mark)*

c) **What substance is passed out of the blood in the capillaries in the body?** .... *(1 mark)*

C

1 Each statement refers to a blood vessel.

Put a tick in the correct box to show which blood vessel the statement refers to. (9 marks)

Statement	Artery	Vein	Capillary
takes blood away from the heart			
carries oxygenated blood			
blood is under high pressure			
is where an exchange of substances takes place			
carries blood to the heart			
contains valves			
has walls one cell thick			
carries deoxygenated blood			
has thick muscular walls			

2 a) What is the main component of plasma?

(1 mark)

....

b) List four other components of plasma.

(4 marks)

....

3 a) Name two types of white blood cell. (1 mark)

....

b) How are the white blood cells different from the red blood cells? (3 marks)

....

4 The diagram shows the heart.

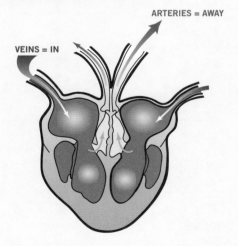

ARTERIES = AWAY

VEINS = IN

2 a) What type of blood vessel is the aorta?

(1 mark)

....

b) The blood returns from the lungs. Describe the route it takes through the heart on its way to the body cells. (4 marks)

....

c) What type of blood returns to the heart from the body? (1 mark)

....

d) Describe the route the blood takes through the heart on its way from the body cells to the lungs. (4 marks)

....

5 Which side of the heart has the thickest walls?

Explain why. (3 marks)

....

6 a) What is tissue fluid? (1 mark)

....

b) What is the function of tissue fluid? (2 marks)

....

Manipulating life

A

1 **Selective breeding is another name for:** (1 mark)

a) artificial selection ☐
b) evolution ☐
c) natural selection ☑
d) variation ☐

2 **Which way of growing plants is an example of cloning?** (1 mark)

a) growing flowers ☐
b) growing seeds ☐
c) fertilising plants ☐
d) taking cuttings ☑

3 **For which disease is genetic modification a promising possible treatment?** (1 mark)

a) Alzheimer's ☐
b) cancer ☐
c) influenza ☐
d) measles ☐

4 **When was the first mammal cloned?** (1 mark)

a) 1896 ☐
b) 1956 ☐
c) 1996 ☑
d) 2006 ☐

5 **Which diseases might be treated using gene therapy?** (1 mark)

a) infectious ☐
b) genetic ☑
c) social ☐
d) self-inflicted ☐

B

1 Dolly the sheep was the first mammal cloned in 1996. She died prematurely in 2003.

Her early death fuelled the debate about the long-term health problems of clones.

Describe the long-term health problems of clones. (4 marks)

....

....

2 a) What is gene therapy? (1 mark)

....

b) What are the two types of gene therapy? (2 marks)

....

c) Explain how gene therapy attempts to cure inherited diseases. (4 marks)

....

....

C

1 a) What is selective breeding? (2 marks)

....

....

b) Why is it sometimes called artificial selection? (1 mark)

....

....

c) Suggest two features farmers might want to breed into their animals and plants. (2 marks)

....

....

d) Why is it more difficult to selectively breed animals than plants? (2 marks)

....

....

2 Genetic modification (GM) is causing huge controversy.

a) Explain some of the risks of GM. (3 marks)

....

....

b) Explain why some people think GM would be safe and necessary. (2 marks)

....

....

c) Explain why some people think GM is unnecessary. (1 mark)

....

....

d) How can crops be modified? (5 marks)

....

....

....

3 Once a large red strawberry has been grown, the plants can be grown by tissue culture.

The diagrams show some of the stages in the process.

Stage 1   Stage 2

Stage 3

a) Explain what is happening at each stage. (3 marks)

1 ....

2 ....

3 ....

b) What are the advantages of growing plants by tissue culture? (4 marks)

....

....

4 a) Describe three ways in which gene therapy can be used to treat cancer cells. (3 marks)

....

....

b) Describe two other ways in which gene therapy can treat cancer. (2 marks)

....

....

Mendel and genetics

A

1 **Who discovered the principles behind genetics?** (1 mark)

a) Jenner ☐
b) Mendel ☐
c) Newton ☐
d) Pasteur ☐

2 **What does genotype mean?** (1 mark)

a) alleles present ☐
b) external fertilisation ☐
c) outward appearance ☐
d) pure breeding ☐

3 **Which allele always shows itself in the phenotype?** (1 mark)

a) dominant ☐
b) heterozygous ☐
c) homozygous ☐
d) recessive ☐

4 **Why did Mendel choose to breed pea plants?** (1 mark)

a) they were in pretty colours ☐
b) they grew quickly ☐
c) they had large peas ☐
d) he could eat them ☐

5 **Which country did Mendel come from?** (1 mark)

a) Austria ☐
b) Belgium ☐
c) France ☐
d) Spain ☐

B

1 **What do the words mean?** (6 marks)

Fill in the boxes. Use words from this list.

dominant   genotype   heterozygous
homozygous   phenotype   recessive

Definition	Word
different alleles	
the stronger allele	
the type of alleles the organism has	
the weaker allele	
what the organism looks like	
both alleles the same	

2 **a)** **What development in 1890 allowed scientists to look at cells in detail?** (1 mark)

....

b) **Which two biological principles could they then investigate?** (2 marks)

....

3 **A pure-breeding yellow canary is bred with a pure-breeding blue canary.**

All the offspring were blue. A blue allele is represented by B.

Complete the genetic diagram below. (5 marks)

Parental genotypes	.... × ....
Gametes	.... or ....
	.... or ....
Offspring generation genotypes	....

C

1 Mendel bred peas. Peas can be round or wrinkled.

a) **Complete the Punnett square.** (4 marks)

R represents the dominant allele (round) and r represents the recessive allele (wrinkled.)

	r	r
R		
r		

b) **What type of pea would these genotypes code for?** (4 marks)

i)   RR ....
ii) Rr ....
iii) rR ....
iv) rr ....

2 Join the boxes to show the meaning of these words. (3 marks)

Word	Meaning
Gametes	Unit of inheritance
Alleles	Sex cells
Gene	Alternative forms of a gene

3 A pure-breeding white gerbil is bred with a pure-breeding black gerbil.

All the F₁ were black. Two black gerbils from the F₁ generation were then bred together.

a) **What is the genotype of the following?**

Use B for the black allele, b for the white.

i)   the original black gerbil .... (1 mark)

ii) the original white gerbil .... (1 mark)

iii) the black F₁ gerbils .... (1 mark)

b) **What was the ratio in the F₂ generation?** (1 mark)

c) **Which allele is recessive?** (1 mark)

4 John has blue eyes. Both his parents have brown eyes.

Use the letter B or b to represent eye colour.

a) i) **What is the genotype of John's father?** (1 mark)

ii) **What is the genotype of John's mother?** (1 mark)

b) **Why can John inherit blue eyes from two brown-eyed parents?** (2 marks)

c) **Is John homozygous or heterozygous for blue eyes? Explain why.** (3 marks)

5 a) **Mendel's pea plants had both male and female reproductive organs. Why was this important?** (2 marks)

b) **What did Mendel conclude from his experiments?** (3 marks)

Growth

A

1 Which gland produces the growth hormone? *(1 mark)*

a) adrenal
b) pituitary
c) thyroid
d) salivary

2 What are stem cells? *(1 mark)*

a) cells that are fully grown
b) cells that have died
c) cells that are not differentiated
d) cells that have no nucleus

3 Cells growing out of control is called: *(1 mark)*

a) division
b) cancer
c) differentiation
d) variation

4 An increase in which factor would increase the growth of plants? *(1 mark)*

a) humidity
b) oxygen
c) shade
d) temperature

5 What is the maximum number of times a cell can divide? *(1 mark)*

a) 10
b) 30
c) 50
d) 70

B

1 Complete the sentences using words from this list. *(9 marks)*

compact   differentiation   limbs   mass   mitosis   shape   specialised   dogs   height

Growth is an irreversible increase in the size or **a)** *height* of an organism. The growth processes in animals include cell division by **b)** .... and **c)** .... , by which cells become **d)** .... for their purpose. Growth involves changes of **e)** .... as well as size.

Animal's bodies tend to grow into a **f)** .... shape, except for their **g)** .... Each particular species of animal has a size range. For example, different breeds of **h)** .... , such as dachshunds and Great Danes, vary greatly in **i)** .... , as do the Great Danes themselves.

2 a) Where are stem cells found? .... *(2 marks)*

b) What happens to stem cells during an organism's life? *(1 mark)*

....

3 The photos show three animals.

a) What do these three animals have in common? *(1 mark)*

....

b) What is this called? .... *(1 mark)*

C

1 The graph shows how the height of people varies.

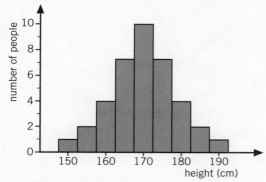

a) How many people have a height of 170 cm? .... (1 mark)

b) What type of variation does this graph show? Explain your answer. (3 marks)

....

c) How is height influenced by the environment? (2 marks)

....

d) Explain what part hormones play in the height of a person. (2 marks)

....

2 a) How can growth be measured? (2 marks)

....

b) Why is measuring live mass inaccurate? (1 mark)

....

c) Why is it difficult to get an accurate mass for an aquatic organism? (1 mark)

....

d) How do you measure dry mass? (2 marks)

....

3 a) What did Hayflick discover while observing cells? (2 marks)

....

....

b) What name did he give to his observation?
.... (1 mark)

c) Explain how Hayflick's observations may exist to prevent cancer. (4 marks)

....

....

4 The diagram shows the end of a root.

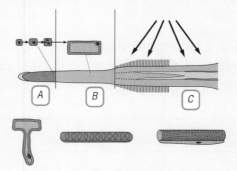

a) Which region on the diagram is where the following take place?

i) cell division? .... (1 mark)

ii) cell elongation? .... (1 mark)

iii) cell differentiation? .... (1 mark)

b) Describe what takes place during the following:

i) cell division (1 mark)

....

ii) cell elongation (1 mark)

....

Mitosis

A

1 **Name the cell that has not yet specialised.** (1 mark)

a) blood
b) nerve
c) stem
d) sperm

2 **A human cell has 46 chromosomes. How many chromosomes will each cell have after mitosis?** (1 mark)

a) 23
b) 46
c) 92
d) 184

3 **When is mitosis not used in dividing cells?** (1 mark)

a) asexual reproduction
b) gamete production
c) formation of clones
d) growth

4 **What is the shape of a DNA molecule?** (1 mark)

a) single strand
b) round
c) double strand
d) oval

5 **How many cells are made from one cell undergoing mitosis?** (1 mark)

a) 1
b) 2
c) 4
d) 8

B

1 **The sentences describe the way that DNA copies itself exactly. They are in the wrong order.**

Put letters in the boxes to show the correct order of the sentences. (6 marks)

A – This leaves the exposed bases.

B – The DNA coils back up into a double helix and the chromosomes have been copied.

C – The helix unwinds and the two strands are unzipped in the middle.

D – In this way two identical strands of DNA are formed.

E – The DNA molecule is made up of two strands coiled together in a double helix shape.

F – New bases present in the cytoplasm join up with the exposed bases.

☐ ☐ ☐ ☐ ☐ ☐

2 **Name the four bases in DNA and state how they pair up.** (5 marks)

....

....

....

C

1 Use the letters A for asexual reproduction and S for sexual reproduction.

Write one letter beside each statement to show which type of reproduction it describes. **(5 marks)**

a) Involves two parents   ....

b) Fertilisation involved   ....

c) Clones are produced   ....

d) Gametes nuclei fuse   ....

e) No variation   ....

2 The following diagram shows one human body cell dividing into two by mitosis.

Parent cell

Daughter cells

a) In the circles write the number of chromosomes you would expect.   **(3 marks)**

b) Describe the appearance of the chromosomes at the beginning of mitosis.   **(1 mark)**

....

c) Why are there 92 chromosomes in the nucleus at one time during division?   **(1 mark)**

....

d) What are chromosomes made of?   **(1 mark)**

....

3 a) Complete the sentences using words from this list.   **(5 marks)**

bone   nerve   paralysis   specialise umbilical cord

Stem cells refer to cells that have yet to **i)** .... into different types of tissue. They are found in adult **ii)** .... marrow or human embryos and the **iii)** .... Adult stem cells do not have the same potential as embryonic stem cells to treat illness.

The idea is that stem cells have the ability to divide and specialise into any tissue needed such as **iv)** .... cells. Treatment with these cells may help conditions such as **v)** ....

b) Where do the stem cells used in research come from?   **(1 mark)**

....

c) Write about three ways in which stem cells can be used.   **(3 marks)**

....

....

d) Some plant cells behave differently to animal cells. Explain how.   **(1 mark)**

....

MITOSIS

Biology

How well did you do? 0-7 Try again   8-18 Getting there   19-29 Good work   30-37 Excellent!

31

Meiosis and fertilisation

A

1 **Where does meiosis take place?** (1 mark)

a) stomach
b) kidney
c) ovary
d) liver

2 **What is the joining of the egg and sperm called?** (1 mark)

a) digestion
b) fertilisation
c) excretion
d) reproduction ✓

3 **How many chromosomes does a human cell have after meiosis?** (1 mark)

a) 23 ✓
b) 46

c) 92
d) 184

4 **Which word describes a gamete?** (1 mark)

a) double
b) diploid
c) haploid
d) single

5 **How many cells are made from one cell undergoing meiosis?** (1 mark)

a) 1
b) 2
c) 4
d) 8

B

1 **The sentences describe meiosis. They are in the wrong order.**
Put letters in the boxes to show the correct order of these sentences. (7 marks)

A – The chromosomes then split up randomly into two cells, so each cell has a mixture of the father's and mother's chromosomes.
B – One of each pair is from the father and the other from the mother.
C – Gametes (sperm or egg cells) are produced.
D – Each with half the number of chromosomes as the original cell (23).
E – There are 23 pairs of chromosomes at the start of meiosis.
F – The chromosomes are then pulled apart to form 4 cells.
G – The chromosomes make an exact copy of themselves (DNA replication).

☐ ☐ ☐ ☐ ☐ ☐ ☐

2 **True or false?**

	True	False	(6 marks)
a) Sexual reproduction involves fertilisation.	☐	☐	
b) Sexual reproduction produces offspring that are genetically identical.	☐	☐	
c) Male and female gametes join to produce a zygote.	☐	☐	
d) Meiosis and fertilisation do not lead to variation.	☐	☐	
e) Mutations may lead to variation.	☐	☐	
f) During fertilisation it is chance which sperm fertilises which egg.	☐	☐	

C

1 The diagram shows how sex is inherited.

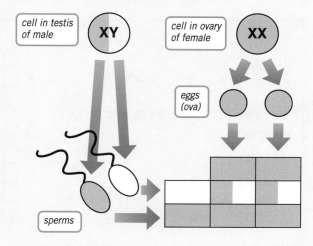

cell in testis of male — XY

cell in ovary of female — XX

eggs (ova)

sperms

a) Which chromosome is found in the eggs and sperms? Write the letter in the eggs and sperms. **(2 marks)**

b) Complete the Punnett square to show the possible chromosome combinations. **(2 marks)**

c) What is the possible ratio of males to females? **(1 mark)**

....

....

....

d) What is the probability of a couple's third child being a boy? **(1 mark)**

....

....

....

2 a) Which pair of chromosomes are the sex chromosomes? **(1 mark)**

....

....

....

b) What is their job? **(1 mark)**

....

....

....

....

c) Which chromosome is only in the male? **(1 mark)**

....

d) How is it different to the other sex chromosome? **(1 mark)**

....

....

....

e) How many chromosomes are there in a testis cell? **(1 mark)**

....

f) How many chromosomes are there in a sperm cell? **(1 mark)**

....

Genes, chromosomes and DNA

A

1 How many pairs of chromosomes are there in a typical human cell? **(1 mark)**

a) 2
b) 23
c) 46
d) 92

2 What are genes made of? **(1 mark)**

a) amino acids
b) chromosomes
c) DNA
d) fats

3 What are chromosomes made of? **(1 mark)**

a) DNA
b) FSH
c) MMR
d) BMI

4 When was the human genome project completed ? **(1 mark)**

a) 1993
b) 1996
c) 2000
d) 2003

5 Which base does the base cytosine always pair up with? **(1 mark)**

a) adenine
b) guanine
c) thymine
d) any

B

1 Complete the sentences. Use words from this list. **(6 marks)**

alleles   chromosomes   enzyme   characteristic   protein   pair

In the centre of nearly all cells is a nucleus containing instructions that control all your characteristics. The instructions are carried on **a)** .... Genes on the chromosome control each particular **b)** .... Different genes control the development of different characteristics. Genes code for a particular **c)** .... or **d)** .... There is a **e)** .... of genes for each characteristic. Different versions of a gene are called **f)** ....

2 A person's DNA fingerprint is unique.

a) Which branch of science uses this technique? **(1 mark)**

....

b) How is DNA fingerprinting used? **(2 marks)**

....

3 a) What is a designer baby? **(1 mark)**

....

b) How is a designer baby created? **(2 marks)**

....

C

1 The sentences describe the steps in protein synthesis. They are in the wrong order. Put letters in the boxes to show the correct order of these sentences. (8 marks)

A – mRNA moves out of the nucleus and carries the copy of the gene to a ribosome.

B – tRNA attaches to the mRNA, bringing with it a particular amino acid.

C – The amino acids are linked together by peptide bonds to form a polypeptide.

D – The sequence of bases is copied and forms a molecule of mRNA.

E – A sequence of three bases on the tRNA will only match against a particular sequence on the mRNA strand.

F – The DNA molecule unwinds to expose a sequence of bases (a gene).

G – The polypeptide forms the particular protein or enzyme required.

H – tRNA, reads the genetic code on mRNA three bases at a time.

☐ ☐ ☐ ☐ ☐ ☐ ☐ ☐

2 Complete the sentences. (5 marks)

The **a)** .... in each cell contains thread-like chromosomes.

The chromosomes occur in **b)** ....

One comes from the **c)** .... and one from the **d)** ....

Each chromosome is made up of a long-stranded molecule called **e)** ....

3 How do genes control the development, structure and function of an organism? (2 marks)

....

....

4 a) What was the aim of the Human Genome Project? (1 mark)

....

b) The project could help the sufferers of some diseases. Name two of these diseases. (2 marks)

....

c) Describe the benefit to the sufferers of these diseases. (1 mark)

....

5 The diagram shows the structure of DNA.

i) ....
ii) ....
iii) ....
iv) ....

a) Label the bases in DNA. (4 marks)

b) The molecule looks like the rungs of a ladder which are coiled together.

What is it called? (1 mark)

....

6 a) Name the two types of RNA used during protein synthesis. (2 marks)

....

b) The gene is copied in the nucleus. To which structure in the cell is the copy taken?

.... (1 mark)

c) What determines the sequence of amino acids in the protein? (1 mark)

....

Homeostasis

A

1 Which poisonous substance is removed by the kidneys? **(1 mark)**

a) amino acids ☐
b) glucose ☐
c) urea ☐
d) water ☐

2 Which part of the body controls our temperature? **(1 mark)**

a) heart ☐
b) brain ☐
c) liver ☐
d) kidneys ☐

3 Which system enables humans to respond to changes in the external environment? **(1 mark)**

a) digestive ☐
b) nervous ☑
c) respiratory ☐
d) skeletal ☐

4 Which gland produces insulin? **(1 mark)**

a) adrenal ☐
b) thyroid ☐
c) pancreas ☑
d) salivary ☐

5 Which is a symptom of diabetes? **(1 mark)**

a) breathlessness ☐
b) cold ☐
c) hot ☐
d) thirst ☐

B

1 Complete the table to show characteristics of hormonal and nervous action. **(6 marks)**

Characteristic	Hormonal	Nervous
Speed of action		
Lasting effect		
Where it acts		

2 a) Describe what happens during vasodilation. **(4 marks)**

....

b) Explain how vasoconstriction is different to vasodilation. **(3 marks)**

....

3 a) Why does a person suffer from diabetes? **(1 mark)**

....

b) What happens in the body when a person suffers from diabetes? **(2 marks)**

....

C

1 Complete the sentences using words from the list. (9 marks)

glucagon	glucose	glycogen
high	hormones	insulin
liver	low	normal

The pancreas is an organ involved in homeostasis; it maintains the level of
a) glucose (sugar) in the blood so that there is enough for respiration. The pancreas secretes two b) hormones into the blood, insulin and glucagon. If blood sugar levels are too c) low , which could be the case after a high carbohydrate meal, special cells in the pancreas detect these changes and release d) .... The e) .... responds to the amount of insulin in the blood and takes up glucose and stores it as f) .... Blood sugar levels return to g) ....
If blood sugar levels are too h) .... , which could be the case during exercise, the pancreas secretes i) .... This stimulates the conversion of stored glycogen in the liver back into glucose, which is then released into the blood. Blood sugar levels return to normal.

2 a) Write down three symptoms of diabetes. (3 marks)

....

b) Apart from diet, how can a person control their diabetes? (1 mark)

....

3 a) How does sweating cool you down? (3 marks)

....
....

b) How do dogs lose heat? (1 mark)

....

c) How does shivering help to keep you warm? (2 marks)

....
....

d) Write about three other ways you can keep warm. (3 marks)

....
....

4 Complete the sentences. (5 marks)

Hormones are a) .... produced by glands known as b) .... glands. Hormones travel in the c) .... to d) .... organs. e) .... is a disease caused by too little of the hormone insulin.

5 True or false? (4 marks)

	True	False
a) The kidneys are organs of excretion.	❏	❏
b) How much water the kidney reabsorbs depends on the hormone FSH.	❏	❏
c) The pituitary gland monitors osmoregulation.	❏	❏
d) In hot weather less water is lost.	❏	❏

How well did you do? 0-20 Try again 21-30 Getting there 31-40 Good work 41-52 Excellent!

37

Farming

A

1 **Which activity is labour intensive in organic farming?** (1 mark)

a) harvesting
b) irrigating
c) planting
d) weeding

2 **What do pesticides do?** (1 mark)

a) kill fungi
b) kill animals
c) kill pests
d) kill weeds

3 **Which is an example of intensive farming?** (1 mark)

a) fish farming
b) organic farming
c) growing cabbages
d) raising free range hens

4 **What is hydroponics?** (1 mark)

a) growth of plants without water
b) growth of plants without soil
c) growth of plants without pesticides
d) growth of plants without fertilisers

5 **What do farmers use to keep their animals free of disease?** (1 mark)

a) antibodies
b) antibiotics
c) antiseptics
d) antigens

B

1 **Complete the sentences.**

Use words from the list. You can use the words more than once. (6 marks)

fertilisers   food   intensive   pesticides

Farming has had to become more **a)** .... to try and provide more **b)** .... from a given area of land.

In order to produce more food from the land, **c)** .... and **d)** .... are needed.

Chemicals called **e)** .... are used to kill insects that eat crops.

Farmers use **f)** .... to replace lost nutrients in the soil.

2 **Biological control is a method used by organic farmers.**

a) **Explain what is meant by biological control.** (1 mark)

....

b) **Give an example of biological control.** (1 mark)

....

c) **What is the advantage of biological control?** (1 mark)

....

d) **What is a disadvantage of biological control?** (1 mark)

....

C

1 The diagram shows how a fish farm could be set up.

a) Name two types of fish that could be farmed in this way. **(2 marks)**

....

b) Where might these farms be found? **(2 marks)**

....

c) The nets have two functions. Describe them. **(3 marks)**

....

....

d) Explain the benefit of restricting movement in these nets. **(3 marks)**

....

....

Complete the sentences by filling in the gaps.

2 Use words from the list. **(6 marks)**

feed   fish   insecticides   lice
parasites   wrasse

Fish reared in fish farms can suffer from
a) .... called fish **b)** ....
One way of dealing with this problem is to use
c) .... to kill the lice or to

introduce another type of **d)** .... ,
called **e)** .... to the nets. The
wrasse will **f)** .... on the lice.

3 Organic farming is thought to be a solution to problems encountered with intensive farming.

a) Apart from biological control, describe how organic farming may solve some of the problems of intensive farming. **(2 marks)**

....

b) What are the disadvantages of organic farming? **(2 marks)**

....

c) Why does organic farming need more labour? **(3 marks)**

....

d) How can organic farmers improve the fertility of their soil? **(3 marks)**

....

4 a) Explain how greenhouses warm up during the day. **(3 marks)**

....

b) Describe how greenhouses keep warm at night. **(2 marks)**

....

....

c) State one problem that may occur in a greenhouse and how it may be controlled. **(3 marks)**

....

....

How well did you do? ✗ 0-20 Try again   21-29 Getting there   30-39 Good work   40-49 Excellent! ✓

The environment

A

1 Which gas increases the greenhouse
effect?   (1 mark)

a) carbon dioxide ☐
b) hydrogen ☐
c) nitrogen ☐
d) oxygen ☐

2 What type of technique is reforestation
and replanting of trees?   (1 mark)

a) conservation ☐
b) destruction ☐
c) energy saving ☐
d) economic ☐

3 What is sustainable development?   (1 mark)

a) keeping things the same ☐
b) maintaining the quality of life for
future generations ☐

c) monitoring resources ☐
d) planting more trees ☐

4 Which body system is missing in
giant tube worms?   (1 mark)

a) circulatory ☐
b) digestive ☐
c) excretory ☐
d) reproductive ☐

5 Replanting forests prevents the
build up of which gas?   (1 mark)

a) carbon dioxide ☐
b) nitrogen ☐
c) oxygen ☐
d) sulphur dioxide ☐

B

1 a) Name three industries where growth has taken place.   (3 marks)

....

b) How does industry contribute to climate change?   (2 marks)

....

2 a) Write down two differences between the developed world and the developing world.   (2 marks)

....

....

b) Why has the population growth in the developed world steadied?   (2 marks)

....

c) What is happening to the population in the developing world?   (1 mark)

....

d) What are the consequences of an increasing population?   (4 marks)

....

C

1 Deep-sea volcanic vents were discovered in the 1970s.

a) Where are they in the ocean? (2 marks)

....

....

b) Describe what happens at these vents, giving examples. (4 marks)

....

....

c) Why does no photosynthesis take place in organisms living in or near these vents? (1 mark)

....

2 Some bacteria use hydrogen sulphide and oxygen to make energy.

a) What is this process called? (1 mark)

....

b) These bacteria live in very high temperatures. How do they survive these temperatures? (1 mark)

....

c) How does the tube worm get its food? (1 mark)

....

d) Name three other animals that live in volcanic vents. (3 marks)

....

....

e) What is unusual about the animals living in these vents? (1 mark)

....

3 a) Why are trees cut down? (2 marks)

....

b) What effect does this have on the environment? (2 marks)

....

4 a) What is deforestation? (1 mark)

....

b) How does deforestation increase the amount of carbon dioxide in the air? (2 marks)

....

....

c) Why are forests sustainable? (1 mark)

....

5 Animals have adapted to living in the Antarctic.

a) Explain how penguins have been able to survive. (3 marks)

....

b) Name three types of animals that can survive in the Antarctic. (3 marks)

....

c) Describe three ways in which animals adapt to the Antarctic conditions. (3 marks)

....

....

How well did you do? ✗ 0-20 **Try again** 21-30 **Getting there** 31-40 **Good work** 41-50 **Excellent!** ✓

41

Atomic structure

A

1 **What are the mass and charge of a proton?** (1 mark)

a) a mass of 1 amu and a charge of 1– ☐
b) a mass of 1 amu and a charge of 1+ ☐
c) a negligible mass and a charge of 1– ☐
d) a mass of 1 amu and no charge ☐

2 **What are the mass and charge of a neutron?** (1 mark)

a) a mass of 1 amu and a charge of 1– ☐
b) a mass of 1 amu and a charge of 1+ ☐
c) a negligible mass and a charge of 1– ☐
d) a mass of 1 amu and no charge ☐

3 **What are the mass and charge of an electron?** (1 mark)

a) a mass of 1 amu and a charge of 1– ☐
b) a mass of 1 amu and a charge of 1+ ☐
c) a negligible mass and a charge of 1– ☐
d) a mass of 1 amu and no charge ☐

4 **What is the mass number of an atom equal to?** (1 mark)

a) the number of protons – the number of electrons ☐
b) the number of protons + the number of neutrons ☐
c) the number of protons ☐
d) the number of electrons ☐

5 **What is the atomic number of an atom equal to?** (1 mark)

a) the number of protons – the number of electrons ☐
b) the number of protons + the number of neutrons ☐
c) the number of protons ☐
d) the number of electrons ☐

B

1 **Complete the following passage.** (12 marks)

Protons and neutrons are found in the **a)** .... of an atom. Protons have a mass of **b)** .... and a charge of **c)** .... Neutrons are also found in the nucleus of atoms. These particles have a mass of **d)** .... and no **e)** .... Electrons are found in **f)** .... around the nucleus. Electrons have a **g)** .... mass and a charge of **h)** .... The electrons fill up shells in order starting with the shell **i)** .... to the nucleus. This is called the **j)** .... shell and can hold up to **k)** .... electrons. In our model, all the other shells can hold up to **l)** .... electrons.

2 **True or false?**

	True	False	(5 marks)
a) In neutral atoms there are always equal numbers of protons and neutrons.	☐	☐	
b) The atomic number of an atom is equal to the number of protons.	☐	☐	
c) Isotopes of the same element have the same numbers of neutrons.	☐	☐	
d) In the periodic table, elements are placed in order of increasing mass number.	☐	☐	
e) In the periodic table, the vertical columns are called groups.	☐	☐	

C

1 The diagrams below show two atoms of the element oxygen.

Atoms of oxygen contain three different types of particle.

The particles in the atoms have been represented by the symbols X, ⊙ and ●.

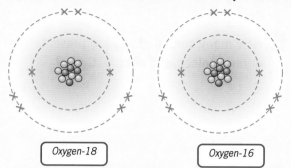

Oxygen-18   Oxygen-16

a) What type of particles do the red crosses on the diagrams represent? (1 mark)

....

b) The yellow dot and blue dot symbols are found in the centre of the two oxygen atoms.

i) What is the centre of an atom called? (1 mark)

....

ii) Which types of particles do the yellow dots and the blue dots represent? (1 mark)

....

c) The table below shows some information about the two oxygen atoms in the diagrams shown above.

	Number of protons	Number of neutrons	Electron structure
$^{16}_{8}O$		8	
$^{18}_{8}O$			

Complete the table to show the number of protons, number of neutrons and the electron structure of each of the oxygen atoms. (5 marks)

Balancing equations

A

1 **What does the state symbol (s) indicate?** (1 mark)

a) salt
b) solid
c) liquid
d) strong

2 **What does the state symbol (l) indicate?** (1 mark)

a) dissolved in water
b) solid
c) liquid
d) it is water

3 **How many oxygen atoms are present in one molecule of CO_2?** (1 mark)

a) 4
b) 3

c) 2
d) 1

4 **How many carbon atoms are present in one molecule of octane, C_8H_{18}?** (1 mark)

a) 18
b) 10
c) 8
d) 26

5 **How many atoms are present in one molecule of octane, C_8H_{18}?** (1 mark)

a) 18
b) 10
c) 8
d) 26

B

1 **True or false?**   True   False   (5 marks)

a) In an equation, the reactants are placed on the right-hand side.
b) Atoms can be made in chemical reactions.
c) Atoms can be destroyed in burning reactions.
d) State symbols show the physical state of the reactants and the products in a reaction.
e) In a balanced symbol equation, there must be equal numbers of each type of atom on both sides of the equation.

2 **Balance these equations.** (5 marks)

You will not need to write in every space shown.

a) ....Na + ...$Cl_2 \rightarrow$ ....NaCl

b) ....N_2 + ...$H_2 \rightarrow$ ....NH_3

c) ....C + ...$CO_2 \rightarrow$ ....CO

d) ....KI + ...$Cl_2 \rightarrow$ ....KCl + ...I_2

e) ....H_2 + ...$Br_2 \rightarrow$ ....HBr

C

1 Geologists are scientists who study rocks. One common rock is called limestone.

Limestone contains the chemical compound calcium carbonate, $CaCO_3$. Many geologists carry bottles of hydrochloric acid. If they think that a rock might be limestone, they test it by placing a couple of drops of hydrochloric acid on the rock. If the rock fizzes, the geologists know that the rock is limestone.

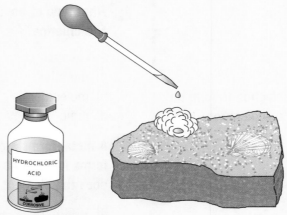

The reaction between calcium carbonate and hydrochloric acid can be summed up by a word equation.

> calcium carbonate + hydrochloric acid → calcium chloride + water + carbon dioxide

a) Why does limestone fizz when hydrochloric acid is dropped on it? **(1 mark)**

....

....

b) Calcium carbonate can be represented by the formula $CaCO_3$.

   i)   How many atoms of calcium are represented in this formula? **(1 mark)**

....

....

   ii) How many atoms of carbon are represented in this formula? **(1 mark)**

....

....

iii) How many different elements are represented in this formula? **(1 mark)**

....

....

c) Balance the symbol equation below to sum up the reaction between calcium carbonate and hydrochloric acid. **(1 mark)**

....$CaCO_{3(s)}$ + ...$HCl_{(aq)}$

→ ....$CaCl_{2(aq)}$ + ...$H_2O_{(l)}$ + ...$CO_{2(g)}$

Ionic and covalent bonding

A

1 Which group of the periodic table has atoms that have a full outer shell of electrons? (1 mark)

a) Group 1
b) Group 2
c) Group 7
d) Group 0

2 If a sodium atom loses an electron to form an ion, what is the charge on a sodium ion? (1 mark)

a) 1+
b) 2+
c) 0
d) 1–

3 If a chlorine atom gains an electron to form an ion, what is the charge on a chloride ion? (1 mark)

a) 1+
b) 2+
c) 0
d) 1–

4 What type of bonding occurs between sodium and chlorine? (1 mark)

a) covalent
b) metallic
c) molecular
d) ionic

5 A metal forms a compound in which the metal forms ions with a 1+ charge. Which group does the element belong to? (1 mark)

a) Group 1
b) Group 2
c) Group 6
d) Group 7

B

1 Complete this passage. (17 marks)

Atoms wish to get a **a)** .... outer shell of **b)** .... Ionic bonding involves the transfer of **c)** .... Metal atoms **d)** .... electrons to gain a **e)** .... charge. Non-metal atoms **f)** .... electrons to gain a **g)** .... charge. An ionic bond is the **h)** .... between these oppositely charged ions.

Sodium chloride is a **i)** .... formed from the metal **j)** .... and the non-metal **k)** .... When sodium reacts with chlorine, sodium atoms **l)** .... an electron to form sodium **m)** .... which have a **n)** .... charge. Chlorine atoms **o)** .... an electron to form chloride ions which have a **p)** .... charge. These ions are then held together by **q)** .... bonds.

2 True or false? True False (5 marks)

a) Ionic bonding involves the sharing of electrons.
b) Oxide ions have a 2+ charge.
c) Electrons have a negative charge.
d) A hydrogen molecule is held together by a strong covalent bond between two hydrogen atoms.
e) A covalent bond is a shared pair of electrons.

C

1 Sodium reacts with chlorine to form the ionic compound sodium chloride. The dot and cross diagrams of a sodium atom and a chlorine atom are shown below.

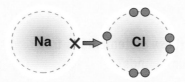

a) Draw a dot and cross diagram to show the electron arrangements in a sodium ion and a chloride ion. **(2 marks)**

b) What is an ion? **(1 mark)**

....

....

c) What is the charge on a chloride ion? **(1 mark)**

....

....

d) What is an ionic bond? **(1 mark)**

....

....

e) Chlorine exists as chlorine molecules, Cl_2. Complete the dot and cross diagram below to show the electron arrangement in a chlorine molecule. **(2 marks)**

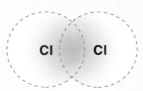

2 Use the words below to complete the table: **(4 marks)**

ionic
electrons
negative
positive

Word	Description
a)	two of these are shared in a covalent bond
b)	the charge on an ion that has lost electrons
c)	the charge on an ion that has gained electrons
d)	the type of bonding in the compound sodium chloride

Ionic and covalent structures

A

1 **Which of these substances is not a simple molecule?** (1 mark)

a) chlorine ☐
b) oxygen ☐
c) graphite ☐
d) water ☐

2 **Which of these statements is true of graphite?** (1 mark)

a) It dissolves in water ☐
b) It conducts electricity ☐
c) It is white ☐
d) All the atoms in graphite are held together by strong bonds ☐

3 **Which of these compounds exists as molecules?** (1 mark)

a) sodium chloride ☐
b) potassium bromide ☐
c) magnesium oxide ☐
d) water ☐

4 **Which of these statements is true of ionic compounds?** (1 mark)

a) They usually dissolve in water. ☐
b) They do not conduct electricity when molten. ☐
c) They have low melting points. ☐
d) They contain bonds which involve shared pairs of electrons. ☐

5 **Which of these types of structures do ionic compounds form?** (1 mark)

a) regular structures ☐
b) simple molecules ☐
c) metallic structures ☐
d) giant covalent structures ☐

B

1 **True or false?** True False (5 marks)

a) Ionic bonding occurs between metal and non-metal atoms. ☐ ☐
b) Ionic bonding involves the sharing of electrons. ☐ ☐
c) Ionic substances can conduct electricity when solid or molten. ☐ ☐
d) Simple molecular compounds cannot conduct electricity. ☐ ☐
e) Graphite conducts electricity because it is a metal at room temperature. ☐ ☐

2 **Complete the following passage.** (12 marks)

Diamond is a form of the **a)** .... carbon. High-quality diamonds are used to make

b) .... like rings and necklaces. Diamonds are also very hard and can be used to

make drills and cutting **c)** .... Diamond's **d)** .... are caused by the

way that the atoms are joined together. In diamond, each **e)** .... atom is bonded to

four other carbon **f)** .... by strong **g)** .... bonds.

Graphite is another form of the **h)** .... carbon. Graphite is used as pencil

i) .... and as a lubricant. Graphite is unusual because it is the only non-metal that

j) .... electricity. In graphite, each carbon atom is bonded to **k)** ....

other carbon atoms by strong covalent bonds. The bonding between **l)** .... is much

weaker than in diamond.

C

1 The diagram below shows the structure of graphite.

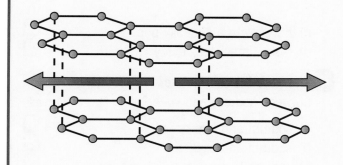

a) Graphite and diamond are both forms of the same element. Name this element. **(1 mark)**

....

b) In graphite, describe the bonding between carbon atoms in the same layer. **(2 marks)**

....

....

....

c) Explain why graphite can conduct electricity. **(1 mark)**

....

....

....

....

2 The diagram below shows the structure of diamond.

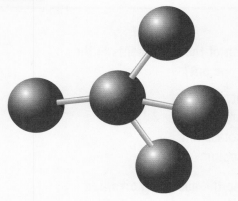

a) Describe the bonding in diamond. **(2 marks)**

....

....

b) Explain why diamonds do not conduct electricity. **(1 mark)**

....

....

c) Explain why diamonds are hard. **(1 mark)**

....

....

3 Use the words below to complete the table:

(4 marks)

graphite   carbon
diamond   sodium chloride

Word(s)	Description
a)	a form of carbon which conducts electricity
b)	an iconic compound
c)	a form of carbon used to make cutting tools
d)	a non-metal element

Group 1 – the alkali metals

A

1 Which of these elements is the odd one out? **(1 mark)**

a) lithium ☐
b) bromine ☐
c) potassium ☐
d) sodium ☐

2 Name the gas given off when a metal reacts with water. **(1 mark)**

a) oxygen ☐
b) helium ☐
c) hydrogen ☐
d) carbon dioxide ☐

3 What is the chemical test for the gas hydrogen? **(1 mark)**

a) relights a glowing splint ☐
b) bleaches damp litmus paper ☐
c) burns with a squeaky pop ☐
d) turns limewater cloudy ☐

4 What are the products of the reaction between sodium and water? **(1 mark)**

a) sodium and hydrogen ☐
b) sodium and oxygen ☐
c) sodium hydroxide and hydrogen ☐
d) sodium hydroxide and oxygen ☐

5 Which of these statements is *not* true of group 1 metals? **(1 mark)**

a) they become more reactive down the group ☐
b) their melting points increase down the group ☐
c) their boiling points decrease down the group ☐
d) they react with non-metals to form coloured compounds. ☐

B

1 True or false? **(5 marks)**

	True	False
a) Lithium, sodium and potassium are denser than water.	☐	☐
b) Potassium burns with a lilac flame.	☐	☐
c) All atoms of alkali metals have just one electron in their outer shell.	☐	☐
d) Universal Indicator will turn purple in a strongly alkaline solution.	☐	☐
e) Alkali metals become more reactive down the group.	☐	☐

2 Complete the following word and symbol equations. **(6 marks)**

a) lithium + water → .... + hydrogen

b) $2Li_{(s)} + 2H_2O_{(l)} \rightarrow 2LiOH_{(aq)} + \ldots\ldots_{(g)}$

c) sodium + ... → sodium hydroxide + hydrogen

d) $\ldots\ldots_{(s)} + 2H_2O_{(l)} \rightarrow 2NaOH_{(aq)} + H_{2(g)}$

e) potassium + water → potassium hydroxide + ...

f) $\ldots\ldots_{(s)} + 2H_2O_{(l)} \rightarrow 2KOH_{(aq)} + H_{2(g)}$

C

1 Group 1 of the periodic table includes the metals lithium, sodium, potassium and rubidium.

The diagram below shows a science teacher placing a piece of sodium metal into a bowl of water.

SODIUM

safety screen

The Group 1 metals
Lithium
Sodium
Potassium
Rubidium

water trough

a) The reaction between sodium and water can be summarised using a word equation.

Complete the word equation below. **(1 mark)**

Sodium + water → .... + ...

b) Why does sodium metal float on water?
(1 mark)

....

....

c) After the reaction had finished, the teacher added some Universal Indicator.

i) What colour did the Universal Indicator turn? **(1 mark)**

....

ii) Why did the Universal Indicator turn this colour? **(1 mark)**

....

d) The metal potassium reacts with water in a similar way to sodium. Describe what you would expect to see when potassium reacts with water. **(2 marks)**

....

....

2 Use the words below to complete the table:
(4 marks)

lithium

hydrogen

alkali metals

sodium

Word(s)	Description
a)	an element with the symbol Na
b)	the name for Group 1 metals
c)	the gas produced when a metal reacts with water
d)	an element that reacts with water to form lithium hydroxide and hydrogen

How well did you do?   ✗ 0-8 **Try again**   9-12 **Getting there**   13-23 **Good work**   24-26 **Excellent!**   ✓

Group 7 – the halogens

A

1 Which halogen is a pale yellow gas? *(1 mark)*

   a) fluorine ☐
   b) chlorine ☐
   c) bromine ☐
   d) iodine ☐

2 Which halogen is the only non-metal element that is a liquid at room temperature? *(1 mark)*

   a) fluorine ☐
   b) chlorine ☐
   c) bromine ☐
   d) iodine ☐

3 How many electrons do halogen atoms have to gain to get a full outer shell? *(1 mark)*

   a) 1 ☐
   b) 2 ☐
   c) 7 ☐
   d) 0 ☐

4 Which halogen is a solid at room temperature? *(1 mark)*

   a) fluorine ☐
   b) chlorine ☐
   c) iodine ☐
   d) bromine ☐

5 Which halogen has the smallest atoms? *(1 mark)*

   a) fluorine ☐
   b) chlorine ☐
   c) bromine ☐
   d) iodine ☐

B

1 Complete the following sentences by crossing out the incorrect word/phrase. *(5 marks)*

   a) Halogen *atoms/ions* have seven electrons in their outer shell.

   b) Halogens are *safe/unsafe* for young children to handle.

   c) Halogens are *coloured/colourless*.

   d) Chlorine atoms *gain/lose* electrons to form ions with a 1– charge.

   e) Halogens *do/do not* conduct electricity when molten.

2 True or false?   True   False   *(5 marks)*

   a) Halogens are safe for young children to use.   ☐   ☐

   b) Oxygen is a halogen.   ☐   ☐

   c) Bromine is a gas at room temperature.   ☐   ☐

   d) Halogens are all colourless gases.   ☐   ☐

   e) Down the group, the halogen atoms get larger.   ☐   ☐

C

1 This question is about halogens.

Use the terms below to complete the table. **(4 marks)**

7
chloride
iodine
bromine

Name	Description
a)	a solid at room temperature
b)	an ion with a 1– charge
c)	a liquid at room temperature
d)	the group in the periodic table where the halogens are found

2 If chlorine gas is bubbled through a solution of sodium bromide, a displacement reaction takes place.

a) Why does chlorine displace bromide from sodium bromide solution? **(1 mark)**

....

....

b) Write the word equation for the reaction. **(1 mark)**

....

....

3 The diagram shows part of the periodic table.

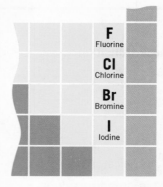

a) What group of the periodic table contains the elements known as the halogens? **(1 mark)**

....

b) Chlorine is a halogen. Give one use of chlorine. **(1 mark)**

....

c) Fluorine is a more reactive halogen than chlorine. Explain why fluorine is more reactive than chlorine. **(1 mark)**

....

....

....

d) If chlorine gas is bubbled through a solution of potassium iodide, a displacement reaction takes place in which potassium chloride and iodine are produced. Write the word equation for the reaction between potassium iodide and chlorine. **(1 mark)**

....

....

Metals

A

1 Which of these transition metals rusts? *(1 mark)*

a) copper ☐
b) iron ☐
c) nickel ☐
d) platinum ☐

2 Which of these properties do you *not* expect of a metal? *(1 mark)*

a) good electrical conductor ☐
b) good thermal conductor ☐
c) can be hammered into shape ☐
d) brittle ☐

3 Which of these properties do you *not* expect of a transition metal? *(1 mark)*

a) hard ☐
b) strong ☐
c) forms white compounds ☐
d) tough ☐

4 What is a mixture of metals called? *(1 mark)*

a) emulsion ☐
b) compound ☐
c) oxide ☐
d) alloy ☐

5 What is the symbol for the element cobalt? *(1 mark)*

a) Cu ☐
b) Co ☐
c) Cp ☐
d) Cb ☐

B

1 True or false? True False *(5 marks)*

a) A catalyst increases the rate of a chemical reaction. ☐ ☐
b) Transition metals are often good catalysts. ☐ ☐
c) Transition metals form white compounds that dissolve to give colourless solutions. ☐ ☐
d) Copper is used in the Haber process. ☐ ☐
e) Nickel is used in the manufacture of margarine. ☐ ☐

2 Complete the table to show the description of some common metals. *(4 marks)*

Name of metal	Description
a)	a metal used to make steel
b)	a catalyst in the Haber process
c)	used in the manufacture of margarine
d)	used to make water pipes and in electrical wiring

C

1 Which of these properties is *not* typical of a metal? Tick one box. (1 mark)

hard wearing ☐
good thermal conductor ☐
strong ☐
low melting point ☐

2 The diagram below shows a section of the periodic table.

2

Group

	1	2											3	4	5	6	7	0
1	H 1																	He 2
2	Li 3	Be 4				'middle block'							B 5	C 6	N 7	O 8	F 9	Ne 10
3	Na 11	Mg 12											Al 13	Si 14	P 15	S 16	Cl 17	Ar 18
4	K 19	Ca 20	Sc 21	Ti 22	V 23	Cr 24	Mn 25	Fe 26	Co 27	Ni 28	Cu 29	Zn 30	Ga 31	Ge 32	As 33	Se 34	Br 35	Kr 36

(Period runs down the left side)

a) What is the name given to the area of the periodic table described in the diagram as the 'middle block'? (1 mark)

....

b) What is the name of the element that has the symbol Fe? (1 mark)

....

c) What is the name given to a mixture of different metals? (1 mark)

....

d) Would you expect nickel, Ni, to be a good thermal conductor? Explain your answer. (2 marks)

....

....

3 Copper is a useful metal.

a) What is the symbol for copper? .... (1 mark)

b) Copper can be used to make saucepans. Which of these properties of copper make it a suitable material to make saucepans from? Circle one answer. (1 mark)

Copper is a good thermal conductor.   Copper is a good electrical conductor.

Copper has an orange–brown colour.   Copper is quite expensive to buy.

How well did you do? ✗ 0-8 Try again   9-13 Getting there   14-17 Good work   18-22 Excellent! ✓

Nano-science and smart materials

A

1 **Thermochromic materials change colour. What causes them to change colour?** (1 mark)

a) changes in temperature
b) changes in pressure
c) changes in electrical current
d) when they are touched

2 **What is the formula of buckminsterfullerene?** (1 mark)

a) C_{12}
b) C_{50}
c) C_{60}
d) C_{100}

3 **Which two metals are found in the alloy nitinol?** (1 mark)

a) nickel and tin
b) nickel and titanium
c) nitrogen and tin
d) nitrogen and titanium

4 **What happens when shape memory alloys are heated up?** (1 mark)

a) They change colour.
b) They return to their original shape.
c) They get cooler.
d) They give off electrical energy.

5 **Why are some nano-materials excellent catalysts?** (1 mark)

a) They are very small.
b) They get used up during chemical reactions but can be cheaply replaced.
c) They have very high surface area to volume ratios.
d) They are incredibly hard.

B

1 **True or false?** True False (5 marks)

a) Nano-particles are smaller than the width of a human hair.
b) Smart alloys always change colour.
c) Thermochromic materials change colour as the temperature changes.
d) Photochromic lenses are used to make sunglasses.
e) Some nano-materials could be dangerous to people.

2 **Complete the passage below.** (11 marks)

Smart materials have one or more **a)** .... that can be dramatically changed by changes to the environment. Some alloys such as **b)** .... have a shape memory. When a

c) .... is applied, these alloys change shape, but when these alloys are

d) .... they return to their original shape.

Thermochromic materials change **e)** .... when they are heated. Thermochromic

f) .... can be used to make objects such as mugs that reveal a new pattern when

g) .... liquids, such as tea, are poured into them.

Photochromic materials change **h)** .... when they are placed in bright

i) .... These materials are widely used to make the lenses for **j)** ....

These lenses adapt to the light conditions. When it is very bright, these materials get

k) ....

C

1 This question is about smart materials.

Smart materials can be used to make products like sunglasses.

Use the words below to complete the table.
(4 marks)

nickel
shape memory alloys
thermochromic materials
photochromic materials

Word(s)	Description
a)	these return to their original shape when they are heated
b)	these change colour when placed in bright light
c)	these change colour when they are heated
d)	this is alloyed with titanium to make nitinol

2 Nano-particles can be used to make catalysts.

a) What is a catalyst? (2 marks)

....

....

....

....

b) Why can nano-particles make very effective catalysts? (2 marks)

....

....

....

....

c) Nano-particles can be used to make strong, lightweight materials. Write down a possible use of a strong lightweight material made using nano-technology. (1 mark)

....

....

....

d) Why can materials made from nano-particles be strong and very lightweight? (1 mark)

....

....

....

3 This mug has been coated with a thermochromic material.

Why is the material used to decorate special mugs like this? (1 mark)

....

....

Relative formula mass

A

1 The relative atomic mass of an element is the average mass of the element's isotopes compared with an atom of which of the following? **(1 mark)**

a) carbon-13
b) carbon-12
c) hydrogen-1
d) oxygen-16

2 What is the percentage composition of carbon in carbon dioxide, CO_2? **(1 mark)**

a) 72%
b) 27%
c) 0.27%
d) 33%

3 What is the percentage of hydrogen in water, H_2O? **(1 mark)**

a) 11%
b) 0.11%
c) 66%
d) 50%

4 What is the percentage of calcium in calcium carbonate, $CaCO_3$? **(1 mark)**

a) 0.4%
b) 60%
c) 0.6%
d) 40%

5 What is the percentage of magnesium in magnesium carbonate, $MgCO_3$? **(1 mark)**

a) 25%
b) 29%
c) 0.29%
d) 75%

B

1 Match the substance to its relative formula mass. **(5 marks)**

Oxygen, O_2	56
Calcium oxide, CaO	44
Magnesium oxide, MgO	32
Carbon dioxide, CO_2	100
Calcium carbonate, $CaCO_3$	40

2 True or false? **(5 marks)**

True   False

a) RAM is used to measure the diameter of different atoms.

b) The relative atomic mass of an element is a weighted average taking into account all the isotopes of the element.

c) The relative formula mass of a substance in grams is called one mole of the substance.

d) The relative formula mass of a compound is worked out by adding together the relative atomic masses of the first two elements in any compound.

e) The percentage by mass of oxygen in water, H_2O, is equal to 50%.

1 In this experiment a student placed a strip of magnesium ribbon into a flask of sulphuric acid. The magnesium reacted with the sulphuric acid. The diagram below shows what happened.

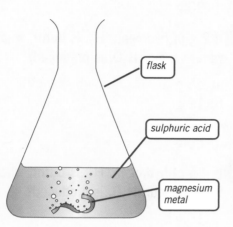

flask

sulphuric acid

magnesium metal

a) How could the student tell that a chemical reaction had taken place? **(1 mark)**

....

....

....

b) This reaction produces the salt magnesium sulphate and the gas hydrogen. Write a word equation for this reaction. **(1 mark)**

....

....

2 You may find the information in the table below useful when answering this question.

Element	Relative atomic mass
magnesium, Mg	24
sulphur, S	32
oxygen, O	16
hydrogen, H	1

a) Calculate the relative formula mass of magnesium sulphate, $MgSO_4$. **(1 mark)**

....

....

b) Calculate the mass of 2 moles of magnesium sulphate, $MgSO_4$. **(1 mark)**

....

....

c) Calculate the percentage of sulphur in magnesium sulphate, $MgSO_4$. **(1 mark)**

....

....

d) Calculate the relative formula mass of sulphuric acid, H_2SO_4. **(1 mark)**

....

....

e) Calculate the percentage of sulphur in sulphuric acid, H_2SO_4. **(1 mark)**

....

....

How well did you do? ✗ 0-6 Try again   7-9 Getting there   10-18 Good work   19-22 Excellent! ✓

Calculating masses

A

1 If 24 g of magnesium is burnt, what mass of magnesium oxide, MgO, is produced? *(1 mark)*

a) 26 g
b) 40 g
c) 20 g
d) 80 g

2 If 12 g of magnesium is burnt, what mass of magnesium oxide, MgO, is produced? *(1 mark)*

a) 26 g
b) 40 g
c) 20 g
d) 80 g

3 If 80 g of calcium is burnt, what mass of calcium oxide, CaO, is produced? *(1 mark)*

a) 96 g
b) 112 g
c) 160 g
d) 80 g

4 If 2 g of hydrogen, H_2, is burnt, what mass of water vapour, H_2O, is produced? *(1 mark)*

a) 16 g
b) 18 g
c) 36 g
d) 80 g

5 If 4 g of hydrogen, H_2, is burnt, what mass of water vapour, H_2O, is produced? *(1 mark)*

a) 16 g
b) 18 g
c) 36 g
d) 80 g

B

1 True or false?

	True	False	(5 marks)

a) Reactions that have a high percentage yield have a high atom economy.
b) The chemical that you have at the start of a chemical reaction is called the product.
c) Side reactions could reduce the yield of a reaction.
d) Some of the products of a reaction can be lost during filtering.
e) The percentage yield of a reaction is a way of measuring the actual yield of the reaction compared with the maximum calculated yield of the reaction.

2 Match the mass of each substance to the number of moles it represents. *(5 marks)*

32 g of oxygen, O_2	1 mole
28 g of calcium oxide, CaO	3 moles
120 g of magnesium oxide, MgO	0.25 moles
11 g of carbon dioxide, CO_2	0.5 moles
75 g of calcium carbonate, $CaCO_3$	0.75 moles

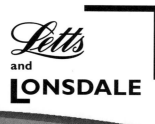

GCSE Success

Workbook
Answer
Booklet

Additional
Science
Higher

Brian Arnold • Elaine Gill • Emma Poole

Answers

Biology

Pages 4–5 Cells

A
1. a) 2. a) 3. b) 4. c) 5. c)

B
1. a) A = cell membrane, B = nucleus, C = cytoplasm
   b) ribosomes and mitochondria
   c) chloroplasts, cell wall and vacuole
2. a) true
   b) true
   c) false
   d) false

C
1.

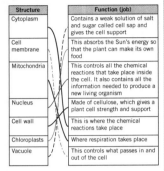

Structure	Function (job)
Cytoplasm	Contains a weak solution of salt and sugar called cell sap and gives the cell support
Cell membrane	This absorbs the Sun's energy so that the plant can make its own food
Mitochondria	This controls all the chemical reactions that take place inside the cell. It also contains all the information needed to produce a new living organism
Nucleus	Made of cellulose, which gives a plant cell strength and support
Cell wall	This is where the chemical reactions take place
Chloroplasts	Where respiration takes place
Vacuole	This controls what passes in and out of the cell

2. A A sperm cell has a tail that enables it to swim towards the egg.
      Or: Its head is also streamlined to aid swimming.
   B Red blood cells have no nucleus so there is more room for oxygen.
      Or: They are also biconcave for maximum surface area.
   C Root hair cells are long and thin to absorb water and minerals from the soil.

3.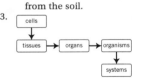
   cells → tissues → organs → organisms → systems

4. a) having many cells
   b) larger, more complex and cells differentiated into many types
   c) amoeba
   d) simple diffusion

Pages 6–7 Diffusion and osmosis

A
1. b) 2. d) 3. a) 4. b) 5. d)

B
1. a) oxygen and glucose
   b) respiration
   c) carbon dioxide and waste
2. a) larger
   b) slower
   c) concentration
   d) diffusion
   e) concentration gradient
3. a) true
   b) false
   c) true
   d) false

C
1. a) an arrow from air into leaf through the stomata in between the guard cells
   b) oxygen and water (vapour)
   c) diffusion
   d) hot, dry and windy

2. a) has become smaller
   b) because water leaves cell by osmosis from region of high water concentration (cell) to a region of low water concentration (sugar solution)
   c) root hair cell
3. a) i) soil, ii) root hairs, iii) minerals, iv) xylem, v) water, vi) cooling, vii) support, viii) evaporation, ix) stomata
   b) three of: light, temperature, amount of air, humidity
   c) guard cells

Pages 8–9 Photosynthesis

A
1. a) 2. b) 3. c) 4. a) 5. b)

B
1. a) $6CO_2 + 6H_2O \rightarrow C_6H_{12}O_6 + 6O_2$
   b) amount of light, amount of carbon dioxide and temperature
2. a) used by plant for respiration and used by animals for respiration
   b) respire to release energy for growth
   c) food for humans, food for animals and fuel (e.g. wood)
3. maximise yields and usefulness, bred to grow in hostile conditions, bred for resistance to disease
4. a) nitrates
   b) phosphates
   c) potassium
   d) magnesium

C
1. a) B = spongy layer
      C = guard cell
      D = stomata
      F = palisade
   b) i)   F/palisade
      ii) D/stomata
      iii) F/palisade
      iv) G and E/xylem and phloem
2. a) As temperature increases, the rate of photosynthesis increases.
   b) As the temperature increases, the rate of photosynthesis drops. The high temperature destroys the enzymes in the chlorophyll.
   c) temperature is too low/it is too cold
   d) heat their glasshouses
3. a) palisade
   b) upper
   c) chlorophyll
   d) green
   e) sunlight

Pages 10–11 Plant hormones

A
1. b) 2. b) 3. c) 4. c) 5. c)

B
1. a) i) geotropism
      ii) phototropism
   b) auxin/hormone
2. a)

Sun

   b) trying to get more light to photosynthesise
   c) on the shaded side
   d) all round the shoot/evenly spread

C
1. a)

shoot
root

   b) shoot always grows away from gravity and root always grows towards gravity
2. a) and b)

auxin

   c) i)   auxin slows the growth of root cells, so root curves downwards
      ii) auxin speeds up the growth of shoot cells, so shoot curves upwards
3. dip cuttings into powder, stimulates root growth, get exact copies/clones of plants
4. a) they kill the broad leaved plants/weeds by making it grow fast
   b) spray synthetic auxin on unpollinated flowers; this makes fruit form without fertilisation, so no seeds are produced
   c) early fruit ripening

Pages 12–13 Pyramids of numbers and biomass

A
1. b) 2. b) 3. d) 4. b) 5. a)

B
1. a) grass
   b)

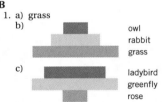
owl
rabbit
grass

   c)
ladybird
greenfly
rose

   d) does not tell us the size of the animals
2. a) sun
   b) photosynthesis
   c) producers
   d) consumers
   e) detritovores

C
1. a) pyramid = 1 mark; labels correct = 3 marks

hawk
voles
caterpillars
tree

   b) $2000 \times 2 = 4000$ g
   c) lower
   d) greater
2. a) primary consumer
   b) respiration and growth
3. a) $100 - (75 + 15) = 10\%$
   b) heat
   c) urine and faeces
   d) eating
4. a) efficiency % = $\frac{\text{amount of useful energy after the transfer}}{\text{total amount of energy before the transfer}} \times 100$
   b) $\frac{100}{1000} \times 100 = 10\%$

Pages 14–15 The carbon cycle

A
1. a) 2. c) 3. b) 4. b) 5. c)

B
1. a) carbon dioxide
   b) carbohydrates, proteins and fats
   c) sun
2. a) carbon dioxide
   b) animals, plants, decomposers
3. a) detritovores
   b) increase the surface area of material for bacteria and fungi to work on
   c) earthworms, maggots and woodlice

C
1. a) A = photosynthesis
      B = respiration
      C = feeding
      D = death
      E = fossilisation
      F = burning/combustion
   b) carbon dioxide
   c) coal, oil, gas
   d) bacteria and fungi
   e) warmth, moisture and oxygen
2. they do not decay, heat and pressure over millions of years make them into fossil fuels
3. a) reduces demand on world resources and reduces problems of disposal
   b) because they are made from oil, which is a non-renewable resource that one day will run out
   c) aluminium
   d) paper
4. a) an organism that feeds on dead and decaying matter
   b) bacteria and fungi

Pages 16–17 The nitrogen cycle

A
1. b) 2. b) 3. c) 4. c) 5. a)

B
1. a) feed on dead and decaying matter, making it easier for decomposers to break it down
   b) animal and plant waste, dead plants and dead animals
   c) bacteria and fungi
   d) to break down dead material into ammonium compounds
2. a) they are taken up by the roots and turned into protein
   b) it is eaten by animals and changed into animal protein

C
1. a) i)   A by bacteria in root nodules
            A by bacteria in soil
      ii) B by bacteria under dead animals and plants
      iii) C by bacteria in waterlogged soil
   b) i)   P on the three arrows leaving 'nitrogen in the air' box
      ii) Q under dead animals and plants
      iii) R on arrow from bacteria in waterlogged soil
   c) animals eat plants, so take in plant protein, which becomes part of their body
   d) when nitrates are washed into the soil before plants can take them up
   e) peas, beans and clover
   f) i)   lightning
      ii) causes nitrogen and oxygen to combine to form nitrogen oxides, which dissolve in rain and are washed into the soil to form nitrates in the soil
2. a) i)   change nitrogen in the air into nitrates

ii) change nitrates into nitrogen gas and ammonia and return it to the atmosphere
iii) change ammonia into nitrates
b) waterlogged soils
c) in soil and in root nodules of plants, e.g. peas/beans

Pages 18–19 Enzymes and digestion

A
1. b) 2. d) 3. a) 4. c) 5. a)

B
1. a) i) catalysts, ii) respiration, iii) photosynthesis, iv) pH, v) temperature, vi) optimum, vii) active site, viii) denatured
b) lock and key
2. cheap and do not need high temperatures
3. a) enzymes
b) shape
c) substrates
d) active site

C
1.

Food	Where digested	End product
Starch	Stomach and small intestine	Fatty acids and glycerol
Protein	Mouth and small intestine	Amino acids
Fats	Small intestine	Glucose

2. a) large insoluble
b) small soluble
c) diffusion
d) enzymes
3. a) proteases and lipases
b) proteases – digest proteins, lipases – digest fats
c) they digest proteins
d) to make chocolate/syrup and convert glucose to fructose
4. teeth chew food and stomach churns food
5. a)

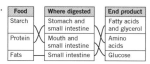

mouth
oesophagus
stomach
large intestine
pancreas
small intestine

b) A – in stomach
B – in mouth
C – in small intestine
D – in rectum
6. it produces bile, which neutralises stomach acid and emulsifies fats, breaking them into smaller pieces/increases the surface area
7. churns up food, mixes food with gastric juices, juices contain enzymes and hydrochloric acid, acid produces the right conditions for enzymes to work

Pages 20–21 Respiration and exercise

A
1. d) 2. a) 3. a) 4. a) 5. b)

B
1. a) the breakdown of glucose to release energy
b) $C_6H_{12}O_6 + 6O_2 \rightarrow 6CO_2 + 6H_2O + energy$
c) mitochondria
d) in every cell and all of the time
e) chemical reactions
2. a) exercise three times a week for 20 minutes
b) respiration

C
1. a) 70 beats/minute (bpm)
b) 60 bpm
c) 5 mins

d) recovery period
e) lines on graph showing higher peak and longer recovery period
f) arteries dilate, deliver oxygen/glucose more quickly, remove carbon dioxide more quickly to/from respiring muscles
2. a) muscles, b) heart, c) oxygen, d) glucose, e) carbon dioxide, f) normal, g) fitness, h) recovery
3. a) use fats and proteins as an energy source instead of carbohydrates
b) constipation, high in fats/cholesterol, clogs up arteries, heart disease, strokes, strain on liver, pressure on kidneys
4. breathing rate and heart rate monitors can be worn on the wrist or around the body by the heart; they produce a continuous measurement before, during and after exercise and also reduce the chance of human error in the readings
5. makes muscles work, absorbs molecules against concentration gradients (active transport), used in chemical reactions, used in growth and repair of cells, makes larger molecules from smaller ones (i.e. proteins from amino acids) and maintains body temperature in warm-blooded animals (mammals and birds)

Pages 22–23 Blood and blood vessels

A
1. b) 2. d) 3. b) 4. d) 5. a)

B
1. a) A = red blood cell
B = white blood cell
C = platelet
b) A carries oxygen
B defence against disease
C clots blood
c) plasma
2. a) They have no nucleus, which leaves more room for haemoglobin + so oxygen.
b) They are small and flexible, so they pass through small blood vessels. Their shape is a biconcave disc, which gives a maximum surface area for absorbing oxygen. They (contain haemoglobin molecules, which) combine with oxygen.
3. a) any organ e.g. liver, brain, kidney
b) oxygenated
c) oxygen

C
1.

Statement	Artery	Vein	Capillary
take blood away from the heart	✓		
carries oxygenated blood	✓		
blood is under high pressure	✓		
is where an exchange of substances takes place			✓
carries blood to the heart		✓	
contains valves		✓	
has walls one cell thick			✓
carries deoxygenated blood		✓	
has thick muscular walls	✓		

2. a) water
b) any four of: soluble food, salts, carbon dioxide, urea, hormones, antibodies and plasma proteins
3. a) phagocytes + lymphocytes
b) have a nucleus, larger and flexible shape

4. a) an artery
b) pulmonary vein → left atrium → left ventricle → aorta
c) deoxygenated
d) vena cava → right atrium → right ventricle → pulmonary artery
5. left side, because it pumps to the body, whereas the right side only pumps to the lungs
6. a) fluid that leaks from the capillaries and bathes the cells
b) delivers food and oxygen and receives waste

Pages 24–25 Manipulating life

A
1. a) 2. d) 3. b) 4. c) 5. b)

B
1. Many cloned animals died even before their embryos were implanted. These embryos had an 'inappropriate expression' of genes. This would lead to a number of deformities if the embryos had been successfully implanted. The embryos would not have reached full term.
2. a) a technique for correcting defective genes responsible for disease and development
b) gene therapy that focuses on the patient and gene therapy that focuses on the eggs and sperm
c) a viral vector carrying a normal gene is inserted into the patient's cells. This gene replaces an abnormal defective gene.

C
1. a) when humans breed in desired features and breed out features not wanted
b) because humans do the selecting not nature
c) increased number of offspring in animals and increased yield in plants
d) because animals breed using sexual reproduction and there is variation in their offspring
2. a) possibility of allergic reactions, that pest and herbicide resistance will spread to wild varieties and reduced biodiversity
b) necessary to feed millions in the developing world to meet the needs of an increasing population
c) enough food is being produced; the problem is with distribution rather than insufficient food supplies
d) Crop characteristics can be improved very quickly. Crops can be made to have resistance to pests and herbicides. Plants can produce artificial substances like oral vaccines. Plants can be made to tolerate drought and other hostile conditions. Tastier or more nutritious crops can be developed.
3. a) stage 1 – few cells taken from selected plant, stage 2 – growth medium prepared and stage 3 – cells placed in growth medium
b) plants grown all year, plants grown quickly, plants grown cheaply and plants that are difficult to grow from seed can be grown
4. a) Specially made genes could be put into the cancer cells to make them more sensitive than normal cells to treatments such as chemotherapy. Genes could

be added into cancer cells and then activated, to produce a poisonous substance (toxin) that kills the cell. Genes could be introduced into cancer cells that make those cells more obvious to the body's own defences (the immune system) so that they are destroyed 'naturally' by the immune system.
b) Damaged genes could be replaced by correctly working versions. New genes could be put into normal cells to make them more resistant to the side-effects of treatment, such as radiotherapy and chemotherapy. This would protect the normal cells from the treatments so that higher doses could be given.

Pages 26–27 Mendel and genetics

A
1. b) 2. a) 3. a) 4. b) 5. a)

B
1.

Definition	Word
different alleles	heterozygous
the stronger allele	dominant
the type of alleles the organism has	genotype
the weaker allele	recessive
what the organism looks like	phenotype
both alleles the same	homozygous

2. a) the microscope
b) cell division and sexual reproduction
3. Parental
genotypes   bb   ×   BB
Gametes   b or b   B or B
Offspring generation
genotypes   Bb

C
1. a)

	r	r
R	Rr/rR	Rr/rR
r	rr	rr

b) i) round
ii) round
iii) round
iv) wrinkled
2.

Word	Meaning
Gametes	Unit of inheritance
Alleles	Sex cells
Gene	Alternative forms of a gene

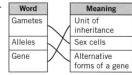

3. a) i) BB
ii) bb
iii) BB
b) 3:1
c) white/b
4. a) i) Bb
ii) Bb
b) They each have the recessive gene for blue eyes (b).
c) homozygous, because he has the recessive bb genes. If he had a dominant B gene, he would have brown eyes.
5. a) because they could self-pollinate or could cross-pollinate with another plant
b) Peas carry a pair of factors for each feature. When the seeds were formed, they inherited one factor from each parent at random. We now call these factors genes. He also came to the conclusion that a characteristic may not show up in an individual but can still be passed on.

Pages 28–29 Growth

A
1. b) 2. c) 3. b) 4. d) 5. c)

B
1. a) mass, b) mitosis,
   c) differentiation, d) specialised,
   e) shape, f) compact, g) limbs,
   h) dog, i) height
2. a) in embryos and bone marrow
      cells of adults
   b) they continue to divide and
      regenerate
3. a) they can re-grow parts of their
      body
   b) regeneration

C
1. a) 10
   b) continuous, because there are
      many different heights in
      between the extremes (or
      'normal')
   c) influenced by nutrition;
      people are smaller when
      undernourished
   d) growth hormone, which is
      produced in the brain,
      influences height
2. a) by looking at the increase in
      length and height of
      organisms, and measuring the
      mass of organisms (live, wet
      mass or dry mass)
   b) because the amount of water
      varies
   c) because water may be left on
      the surface of the body
   d) measure mass in dead
      organisms after they have
      been dried in an oven
3. a) that cells only divided about
      50 times before they died and
      that the cells showed signs of
      old age as they approached
      this number of divisions
   b) the Hayflick Limit
   c) when cells reach the Hayflick
      Limit,
      tumour cells would stop
      dividing
      and die off;
      some cancers have found a
      way round this
4. a) i) A
      ii) B
      iii) C
   b) i) mitosis/cell divides into
         two
      ii) cell vacuole absorbs water
         and swells

Pages 30–31   Mitosis
A
1. c) 2. b) 3. b) 4. c) 5. b)
B
1.

E	C	A	F	D	B

2. Adenine pairs with thymine and
   cytosine pairs with guanine (1
   mark for each base and 1 mark
   for the pairings)
C
1. a) S
   b) S
   c) A
   d) S
   e) A
2. a) 46 in all three cells
   b) mass of tangled threads
   c) because chromosomes
      replicate themselves before
      separating
   d) DNA
3. a) i) specialise
      ii) bone
      iii) umbilical cord
      iv) nerve
      v) paralysis
   b) human embryos
   c) used to replace tissue that has
      lost its function i.e. heart;
      used to treat genetic diseases
      by being implanted into the
      donor
      before the genetic disease has
      developed;
      treating brain disease

---

   d) they can continue to grow
      throughout life

**Pages 32–33   Meiosis and
fertilisation**
A
1. c) 2. b) 3. a) 4. c) 5. c)
B
1.

E	B	G	A	F	D	C

2. a) true
   b) false
   c) true
   d) false
   e) true
   f) true
C
1. a) X in both eggs, X in one sperm
      and Y in the other sperm
   b) XX in bottom boxes and XY in
      top boxes
   c) 1:1 or 2:2 or 50:50
   d) 50:50
2. a) 23rd pair
   b) to determine whether it's a
      boy or girl
   c) Y
   d) shorter
   e) 46
   f) 23

**Pages 34–35   Genes,
chromosomes and DNA**
A
1. b) 2. c) 3. a) 4. d) 5. b)
B
1. a) chromosomes,
   b) characteristic, c) enzyme,
   d) protein, e) pair, f) alleles
2. a) forensic science
   b) identify suspects, clear
      wrongly accused, identify
      paternity, match donor to
      recipients
3. a) a baby with specific features
   b) embryos are screened for
      disease or gender then
      implanted
C
1.

F	D	A	H	B	E	C	G

2. a) nucleus
   b) pairs
   c) mother
   d) father
   e) DNA
3. genes are instructions for a
   protein and proteins control our
   characteristics
4. a) to identify all the genes in
      human DNA
   b) Alzheimer's disease and
      breast cancer
   c) improved/earlier diagnosis
5. a) i) guanine
      ii) thymine
      iii) adenine
      iv) cytosine
   b) double helix
6. a) messenger RNA and transfer
      RNA
   b) ribosome
   c) the order of bases on the
      mRNA

Pages 36–37   Homeostasis
A
1. c) 2. b) 3. b) 4. c) 5. d)
B
1.

Characteristic	Hormonal	Nervous
Speed of action	slower	fast
Lasting effect	long lasting	doesn't last long
Where it acts	may affect several organs	affects a specific place

2. a) Blood vessels at the surface of
      the skin widen,
      allowing more blood to flow
      to the surface,
      which makes skin looks red.

   Heat is lost as it radiates from
   the skin.
   b) blood vessels at surface
      constrict, skin looks pale, less
      heat lost
3. a) pancreas does not make
      enough insulin
   b) blood sugar levels increase;
      not enough glucose gets to the
      cells for respiration
C
1. a) glucose, b) hormones, c) high,
   d) insulin, e) liver, f) glycogen,
   g) normal, h) low, i) glucagon
2. a) tiredness, weight loss, thirst,
      even death
   b) by injecting themselves with
      insulin
3. a) sweat forms at surface of skin,
      sweat evaporates, evaporation
      takes heat from body
   b) by panting
   c) muscles contract, producing
      heat to keep you warm
   d) sweat glands stop producing
      sweat, increased respiration
      produces heat, exercise. Hairs
      stand on end trapping layer of
      air against skin. Air is a good
      insulator.
4. a) chemical messengers
   b) endocrine
   c) blood
   d) target
   e) Diabetes
5. a) true
   b) false
   c) true
   d) false

Pages 38–39   Farming
A
1. b) 2. c) 3. a) 4. b) 5. b)
B
1. a) intensive, b) food,
   c) pesticides/fertilisers,
   d) fertilisers/pesticides,
   e) pesticides, f) fertilisers
2. a) use of another animal that
      eats pests/natural predators
   b) ladybirds eating greenfly
   c) no harmful effects
   d) not so effective/predator eats
      other organisms/interferes
      with food chain
C
1. a) salmon and trout
   b) in a lake and in the sea
   c) protect the fish from
      predators (such as seals or
      seagulls), restrict movement
   d) maximises the energy transfer
      from the food, less energy is
      used in movement, fish put
      on weight
2. a) parasites, b) lice,
   c) insecticides, d) fish,
   e) wrasse, f) feed
3. a) set aside land for wildlife and
      use manure as fertiliser
   b) less food per area of land,
      expensive
   c) does not use
      fertilisers/herbicides/pesticid
      es, therefore more weeds
      grow, needs more people
   d) grow plants that can fix
      nitrogen, do not harvest,
      plough them in, use manure
4. a) Greenhouses work by
      trapping heat from the sun.
      The floor of the greenhouse
      heats up and heats the layer
      of air above it. This hot air
      rises up to the top of the
      greenhouse. This hot air is
      replaced by cooler air that, in
      turn, is also heated and rises.
      The warmer air at the top of
      the greenhouse is replaced
      and sinks back to the bottom,
      where it is heated up again.
   b) The ground and air absorb
      sufficient heat during the day

---

   to keep the greenhouse
   relatively warm at night.
   Additional heating systems
   can be used because the
   amount of sunlight varies
   from day to day.
   c) One problem that does occur
      in a greenhouse is that of
      pests. These can be controlled
      by using pesticides or
      biological pest controls
      (predators specific to the
      pest).

Pages 40–41   The environment
A
1. a) 2. a) 3. b) 4. b) 5. a)
B
1. a) mining, transport and power
      generation
   b) release harmful gases, which
      contribute to acid rain and
      pollution
2. a) developed world consumes
      more energy and produces
      more waste
   b) education and family
      planning
   c) it is rising
   d) more pressure is put on
      natural resources, such as
      fossil fuels, and the land;
      more and more land is being
      built on; more land is being
      intensively farmed to produce
      food; forests are disappearing;
      species are under threat from
      hunting and over fishing;
      pollution of land and water is
      increasing
C
1. a) mid-ocean ridges and on
      ocean floor
   b) fluids and gases
      from the earth's crust seep
      through, e.g. methane
      or hydrogen sulphide
   c) because there's no light for
      photosynthesis
2. a) chemosynthesis
   b) bacterial proteins are resistant
      to the heat
   c) bacteria inside it provide food
   d) giant clams, crabs, shrimps
   e) they are usually large
3. a) for use as fuel and to clear
      land for building
   b) plant and animal habitats are
      destroyed and soil erosion
      increases
4. a) destruction of forests
   b) reduces the number of
      photosynthesising organisms
      and burning trees gives off
      carbon dioxide
   c) they can be
      replaced/replanted
5. a) have a compact body shape
      and have a thick skin
      to retain body heat/prevent
      loss of body heat
   b) whales, seals, birds
   c) have an insulating layer of
      fat/special chemicals in their
      blood that prevent them from
      freezing/
      compact body shape to retain
      body heat

Chemistry
Pages 42–43   Atomic structure
A
1. b) 2. d) 3. c) 4. b) 5. c)
B
1. a) nucleus , b) 1 , c) 1+ , d) 1 ,
   e) charge , f) shells/levels ,
   g) negligible , h) 1– , i) closest,
   j) first , k) two , l) eight
2. a) false
   b) true
   c) false
   d) false
   e) true

C
1. a) electrons
   b) i) nucleus
      ii) protons and neutrons
   c)

	Number of protons	Number of neutrons	Electron structure
$^{16}_{8}O$	8	8	2, 6
$^{18}_{8}O$	8	10	2, 6

Pages 44–45 Balancing equations
A
1. b) 2. c) 3. c) 4. c) 5. d)
B
1. a) false
   b) false
   c) false
   d) true
   e) true
2. a) $2Na + Cl_2 \rightarrow 2NaCl$
   b) $N_2 + 3H_2 \rightarrow 2NH_3$
   c) $C + CO_2 \rightarrow 2CO$
   d) $2KI + Cl_2 \rightarrow 2KCl + I_2$
   e) $H_2 + Br_2 \rightarrow 2HBr$
C
1. a) a gas/carbon dioxide is made
   b) i) 1
      ii) 1
      iii) 3
   c) $CaCO_{3(s)} + 2HCl_{(aq)} \rightarrow CaCl_{2(aq)} + H_2O_{(l)} + CO_{2(g)}$

Pages 46–47 Ionic and covalent bonding
A
1. d) 2. a) 3. d) 4. d) 5. a)
B
1. a) full, b) electrons, c) electrons, d) lose, e) positive, f) gain, g) negative, h) attraction, i) compound, j) sodium, k) chlorine, l) lose, m) ions, n) positive, o) gain, p) negative, q) ionic
2. a) false
   b) false
   c) true
   d) true
   e) true
C
1. a)
   b) an atom/group of atoms that has gained/lost electrons and so has a charge
   c) 1–
   d) attraction between oppositely charged ions.
   e)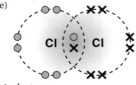
2. a) electrons
   b) positive
   c) negative
   d) ionic

Pages 48–49 Ionic and covalent structures
A
1. c) 2. b) 3. d) 4. a) 5. a)
B
1. a) true
   b) false
   c) false
   d) true
   e) false
2. a) element, b) jewellery, c) tools, d) properties, e) carbon, f) atoms, g) covalent, h) element, i) 'lead', j) conducts, k) three, l) layers

---

C
1. a) carbon
   b) Each carbon atom is bonded to three other carbon atoms by strong covalent bonds.
   c) The bonding between layers is weak, and the electrons in these weak bonds can move.
2. a) Each carbon atom is bonded to four other carbon atoms by strong covalent bonds.
   b) no electrons in weak bonds to move
   c) They have lots of strong bonds.
3. a) graphite
   b) sodium chloride
   c) diamond
   d) carbon

Pages 50–51 Group 1 – the alkali metals
A
1. b) 2. c) 3. c) 4. c) 5. b)
B
1. a) false
   b) true
   c) true
   d) true
   e) true
2. a) lithium hydroxide
   b) H_2
   c) water
   d) $2Na$
   e) hydrogen
   f) $2K$
C
1. a) sodium hydroxide + hydrogen
   b) It is less dense than water.
   c) i) purple
      ii) because sodium hydroxide forms an alkaline solution
   d) fizzing/bubbling, floats on water, lilac flame
2. a) sodium
   b) alkali metals
   c) hydrogen
   d) lithium

Pages 52–53 Group 7 – the halogens
A
1. a) 2. c) 3. a) 4. c) 5. b)
B
1. a) atoms
   b) unsafe
   c) coloured
   d) gain
   e) do not
2. a) false
   b) false
   c) false
   d) false
   e) true
C
1. a) iodine
   b) chloride
   c) bromine
   d) 7
2. a) Chlorine is more reactive than bromine.
   b) chlorine + sodium bromide $\rightarrow$ bromine + sodium chloride
3. a) 7
   b) one of: purification of water, manufacture of hydrochloric acid, manufacture of PVC
   c) Fluorine has fewer shells of electrons than chlorine, so when it reacts and gains an electron, this electron goes into a shell closer to the nucleus.
   d) potassium iodide + chlorine $\rightarrow$ potassium chloride + iodine

Pages 54–55 Metals
A
1. b) 2. d) 3. c) 4. d) 5. b)
B
1. a) true
   b) true
   c) false

---

   d) false
   e) true
2. a) iron
   b) iron
   c) nickel
   d) copper
C
1. low melting point
2. a) transition metals
   b) iron
   c) alloy
   d) yes – it is a metal so it has free/delocalised electrons that can move
3. a) Cu
   b) Copper is a good thermal conductor

Pages 56–57 Nano-science and smart materials
A
1. a) 2. c) 3. b) 4. b) 5. c)
B
1. a) true
   b) false
   c) true
   d) true
   e) true
2. a) properties, b) nitinol, c) force, d) heated/warmed, e) colour, f) materials/substances, g) hot/cold/warm, h) colour, i) light/conditions, j) sunglasses, k) darker
C
1. a) shape memory alloys
   b) photochromic materials
   c) thermochromic materials
   d) nickel
2. a) A substance that speeds up a reaction but is not used up by the reaction.
   b) Many reactions take place at the surface of a catalyst. Nano-particles are very effective catalysts because they have a high surface area to volume ratio, which allows lots of reactions to take place.
   c) for example, planes or bridges
   d) because of the precise way the atoms are arranged
3. When hot/warm liquid is poured into the mug a design is revealed.

Pages 58–59 Relative formula mass
A
1. b) 2. b) 3. a) 4. d) 5. b)
B
1.

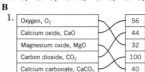

2. a) false
   b) true
   c) true
   d) false
   e) false
C
1. a) bubbles/fizzing
   b) magnesium + sulphuric acid $\rightarrow$ magnesium sulphate + hydrogen
2. a) 120
   b) 240 g
   c) 27%
   d) 98
   e) 32.7%

Pages 60–61 Calculating masses
A
1. b) 2. c) 3. b) 4. b) 5. c)
B
1. a) true
   b) false
   c) true
   d) true
   e) true

---

   d) false
   e) true
2. a) iron
   b) iron
   c) nickel
   d) copper
C
2.

32 g of oxygen, O_2		1 mole
28 g of calcium oxide, CaO		3 moles
120 g of magnesium oxide, MgO		0.25 moles
11 g of carbon dioxide, CO_2		0.5 moles
75 g of calcium carbonate, $CaCO_3$		0.75 moles

C
1. a) 100
   b) calcium carbonate + hydrochloric acid $\rightarrow$ calcium chloride + water + carbon dioxide
   c) $CaCO_{3(s)} + 2HCl_{(aq)} \rightarrow CaCl_{2(aq)} + H_2O_{(l)} + CO_{2(g)}$
   d) number of moles in 5 g of calcium carbonate = 0.05 moles, mass of carbon dioxide produced = 2.2 g
   e) number of moles in 5 g of calcium carbonate = 0.05 moles, mass of calcium chloride produced = 5.55 g
2. 4.5 g

Pages 62–63 Reversible reactions
A
1. c) 2. c) 3. d) 4. b) 5. c)
B
1. a) true
   b) false
   c) false
   d) false
   e) false
2. a) A and B are the **reactants** of the forward reaction.
   b) The backward reaction is **endothermic**.
   c) Increasing the pressure **increases** the yield of the product.
   d) Increasing the temperature **increases** the rate of reaction.
   e) At equilibrium, **the reactions still occur but the forward reaction happens at the same rate as the backward reaction**.
C
1. a) i) sulphur dioxide and oxygen
      ii) no effect
   b) It is a reversible reaction.
   c) i) decrease
      ii) nothing can enter or leave

Pages 64–65 The Haber process
A
1. b) 2. d) 3. b) 4. c) 5. c)
B
1. a) true
   b) false
   c) false
   d) false
   e) false
2. a) nitrogen, b) formula, c) Haber, d) natural, e) air, f) reversible, g) forward, h) reverse/backwards, i) nitrogen, j) recycled/reused
C
1. a) A system in which nothing can enter or leave.
   b) When the rate of the forward reaction is equal to the rate of the backward reaction/where there is no change in the concentrations of the reactants and the products.
   c) i) increases
      ii) decreases
   d) increases
   e) i) increases
      ii) no effect
2. a) nitrogen + hydrogen $\rightleftharpoons$ ammonia
   b) $N_2 + 3H_2 \rightleftharpoons 2NH_3$
   c) To reduce costs/reduce waste/preserve resources.

Pages 66–67 Rates of reaction
A
1. a) 2. d) 3. b) 4. a) 5. a)

B

1. a)

one mark for labelled axes
one mark for even scales
one mark for correctly
plotting the points
one mark for best of fit line

   b) 0–10 s/at the start
   c) after 50 s

C

1. a) gas syringe/mass
balance/measuring cylinder
(with calibration) and collect
over water
   b) timer/stopwatch/clock
   c) amount of reactant or product
and the time taken for the
reaction to complete
   d) Particles have more energy
and so move faster. Particles
therefore have more
collisions. More of these
collisions are successful, so
the rate of reaction increases.

Pages 68–69   Exothermic and endothermic reactions

A

1. c) 2. d) 3. c) 4. c) 5. b)

B

1. a) true
   b) false
   c) false
   d) false
   e) true
2. a) given out to the surroundings
   b) made and broken
   c) heat energy
   d) exothermic
   e) endothermic

C

1. a) methane + oxygen → carbon
dioxide + water (vapour)
   b) 4 times 413 plus 2 times 498 =
2648 kJ mol^{-1}
   c) 2 times 805 plus 4 times 464 =
3466 kJ mol^{-1}
   d) More energy is given out
(3466 kJ mol^{-1}) when new
bonds are formed than is
taken in when old bonds are
broken (2648 kJ mol^{-1}).
2. 2887 kJ mol^{-1}

Pages 70–71   Electrolysis of sodium chloride solution

A

1. c) 2. d) 3. b) 4. c) 5. b)

B

1. a) hydrogen
   b) sodium chloride solution
   c) negative electrode
   d) positive electrode
   e) chlorine
2. a) true
   b) false
   c) true
   d) false
   e) true

C

1. a) chlorine
   b) one of: to make bleach, to
sterilise water, in the
production of PVC or to
produce hydrochloric acid
   c) $2Cl^- - 2e^- \rightarrow Cl_2$
   d) hydrogen
   e) manufacture of margarine
   f) $2H^+ + 2e^- \rightarrow H_2$
   g) sodium hydroxide
   h) one of: to make soaps and

detergents or to make rayon
and acetate fibres
2. a) hydrogen
   b) sodium chloride
   c) chlorine
   d) margarine

Pages 72–73   Acids, bases and neutralisation

A

1. d) 2. a) 3. b) 4. c) 5. b)

B

1. a) salt
   b) potassium nitrate
   c) potassium sulphate
   d) calcium chloride
   e) water
2. a) true
   b) false
   c) false
   d) true
   e) false

C

1. a) colourless
   b) blue
   c) yellow
   d) Universal Indicator
   e) green
   f) Universal Indicator and
methyl orange
   g) Universal Indicator and
phenolphthalein

Pages 74–75   Making salts

A

1. d) 2. a) 3. c) 4. b) 5. a)

B

1. a) magnesium chloride,
   b) hydrogen, c) reactive,
   d) copper sulphate, e) salts,
   f) water, g) magnesium chloride,
   h) carbon dioxide
2. a) hydrogen
   b) magnesium
   c) copper sulphate
   d) carbon dioxide
   e) water

C

1. b) The unreacted copper
carbonate is removed by
filtering.
   c) The solution is poured into an
evaporating dish.
   d) It is heated until the first
crystals appear.
   e) The solution is left for a few
days for the copper chloride
to crystallise.
2. a) zinc chloride, water, carbon
dioxide
   b) bubbling/fizzing
   c) stops bubbling
   d) filtering
   e) evaporate the
water/crystallise the salt
3. a) magnesium chloride
   b) magnesium nitrate
   c) calcium sulphate
   d) copper chloride

Pages 76–77   Chemical tests

A

1. d) 2. a) 3. c) 4. b) 5. c)

B

1. a) carbon dioxide, b) bubbled,
   c) cloudy/milky, d) lighted,
   e) squeaky pop, f) oxygen, g) air,
   h) glowing, i) relights, j) gas,
   k) damp, l) bleached

C

1. a) sugar → alcohol (ethanol)
+ carbon dioxide
   b) i) limewater
      ii) limewater goes cloudy
2. a) limewater
   b) carbon dioxide
   c) oxygen
   d) chlorine
3. Use damp red litmus paper.
If the gas is chlorine, the damp
red litmus paper will be
bleached.

Pages 78–79   Water

A

1. b) 2. b) 3. a) 4. b) 5. c)

B

1. a) false
   b) true
   c) false
   d) true
   e) true
2. a) water
   b) planet
   c) oceans
   d) salts
   e) polluted/contaminated
   f) reservoirs
   g) filtered
   h) chlorine

C

1. a) bleach
   b) water softener
   c) detergent
   d) optical brighteners
2. a) clothes could be damaged
   b) Step 1 – Add solvent
Step 2 – Remove solvent
Step 3 – Press clothes
   c) the forces of attraction
between stain molecules are
greater than the forces of
attraction between stain
molecules and water
molecules
   d) the forces of attraction
between water molecules and
stain molecules are greater
than the forces of attraction
between stain molecules

Pages 80–81   Uses of oil and alcohol

A

1. b) 2. b) 3. c) 4. b) 5. a)

B

1. a) true
   b) false
   c) false
   d) true
   e) false
2. a) solids
   b) bonds
   c) saturated
   d) cholesterol
   e) liquids
   f) oils
   g) bonds
   h) unsaturated
   i) hydrogenation
   j) cakes

C

1. a) seeds and nuts
   b) get fat/heart disease, etc.
   c) i) C=C
      ii) add bromine water
      iii) it decolourises
2. a) liquid
   b) nickel
   c) covalent
   d) unsaturated

Physics
Pages 82–83   Speed, velocity and acceleration

A

1. c) 2. c) 3. d) 4. d) 5. a)

B

1. a) The speed of an object tells us
how fast it is moving. The
velocity of an object tells us
how fast it is moving **and** in
which direction.
   b) e.g. 5 m/s
   c) e.g. 5 m/s northwards
   d) Speed = Distance
travelled/Time taken
   e) 80 km/h
   f) 20 km

C

1. a) 10 km/h/s
   b) 1000 km
   c) 9 hours
   d) 300 km/h
   e) The second aircraft will land

first. It will land one hour
before the first aircraft.
2. a) 5 m/s^2
   b) 3 s
   c) 6 s

Pages 84–85   Graphs of motion

A

1. d) 2. b) 3. c) 4. a) 5. a)

B

1. a) 500 m
   b) 150 s
   c) 6 m/s
   d) 2 m/s

C

1. a)

   b) Plane accelerates uniformly
from rest for first 60 s of
journey. It then continues to
accelerate but at a lower rate
until it reaches a speed of 270
km/h. It travels at this speed
for 60 s. It then decreases its
speed to 130 km/h and travels
at this speed for the next 60 s.
   c) 4 500 m (4.5 km)
   d) 3 km/h/s

Pages 86–87   Balanced and unbalanced forces

A

1. b) 2. c) 3. d) 4. c) 5. b)

B

1. a) i)   2.5 m/s^2
      ii) 250 m/s^2
      iii) 400 m/s^2
   b) i)   25 N
      ii) 45 N

C

1. a) weight
   b) weight acts vertically
downwards, upthrust acts
vertically upwards
   c) The forces are balanced. The
beaker is stationary.
   d) The weight of the beaker and
its contents has increased. As
a result the beaker sinks
deeper into the water. The
upthrust increases until the
two forces are again balanced.
   e) The weight is bigger than the
upthrust.
2. a) 5 m/s^2
   b) 75 m/s

Pages 88–89   Frictional forces and terminal velocity

A

1. c) 2. d) 3. c) 4. c) 5. a)

B

1. a)–ii), b)–i), c)–iv), d)–vi), e)–iii),
f)–v)

C

1. a) When she is travelling at a
constant speed her drag
forces and her propulsive
forces are balanced. When she
leans forward her drag forces
decrease so she accelerates.
As her speed increases the
drag forces increase and
eventually they again balance
and the cyclist will travel
again at a constant speed.
   b) They could wear tight fitting
clothing and helmets to aid
streamlining. They should
ride one team member close
behind another so that only
the front rider experiences the
full impact of the air

resistance. The others save energy and therefore should be able to cycle faster when it is their turn to be up front.
2. a) 5000 N
   b) 5 m/s^2.
   c) As the speed of the car increases the drag forces also increase so the acceleration of the car also decreases.
   d) At 160 km/h the propulsive force from the car's engine is balanced by all the frictional forces resisting the motion of the car.
   e) More streamlined shape and bigger propulsive engine (more propulsive force)

Pages 90–91   Stopping distance
A
1. c) 2. d) 3. d) 4. b) 5. c)
B
1. a) braking, b) force, c) reaction, d) tiredness, e) visibility, f) vehicle, g) mass, h) speed, i) friction, j) tyres
2. age, tiredness, taking drugs, drinking alcohol
C
1. a) i) The larger the mass of the car the greater the braking distance needed
      ii) The greater the speed of the car the larger the braking distance needed
      iii) The smoother the road surface the greater the braking distance needed
      iv) The smoother the surfaces of the tyres the greater the braking distance needed
   b) i) The greater the speed of the car the larger the thinking distance
      ii) The poorer the visibility the larger the thinking distance
      iii) The large the reaction time of the driver the larger the thinking distance.
   c) i) The older Brian is the slower his reaction time is likely to be.
      ii) Noisy passengers will make it hard for Brian to concentrate on his driving and so his reaction time may increase.
      iii) If Brian is tired his reactions will be slower.

Pages 92–93   Work and power
A
1. b) 2. d) 3. b) 4. a) 5. a)
B
1. a) i) 30 J
      ii) 60 kJ
      iii) 90 kW
   b) i) 3 kW
      ii) 4.5 kW
C
1. a) 6000 J or 6 kJ
   b) 300 W
2. a) 10 kJ
   b) 5 s
3. 50 s

Pages 94–95   Kinetic energy and potential energy
A
1. b) 2. d) 3. a) 4. b) 5. a)
B
1. a) 4000 J
   b) 225 kJ
   c) 200 MJ
2. a) 10 kJ
   b) 1.8 MJ
   c) 50 J

C
1. a) gravitational potential energy
   b) 4 J
   c) It changes into kinetic energy.
   d) 6.3 m/s
   e) kinetic energy changes back into potential energy
   f) some energy is lost during the collision with the ground
   g) The ball would not bounce as high after hitting the ground for the first time. The total number of times the ball bounces would be less.
   h) Air resistance now becomes important. Some of the potential energy of the ball is used to overcome friction so less of it is changed into kinetic energy.

Pages 96–97   Momentum
A
1. c) 2. c) 3. b) 4. b) 5. d)
B
1. a) 15 000 kgm/s
   b) 600 kgm/s
2. a) 2000 kg
   b) 200 kg
3. a) 20 m/s
   b) 40 m/s
C
1. a) Part of a car which is designed to become squashed during a collision
   b) Work is done as the car crumples ie some of the energy of the collision is removed
   c) seatbelts and air bags
   d) Both increase the time during the crash when momentum is decreasing. This reduces the sizes of the decelerating forces applied to the passengers.
   e) 2400 kgm/s
   f) 4800 N

Pages 98–99   Collisions and explosions
A
1. b) 2. b) 3. a) 4. c) 5. d)
B
1.

A	R	O	C	K	E	T	D	F	M
B	E	X	P	L	O	S	I	O	N
C	C	O	L	L	I	S	I	O	N
M	O	M	E	N	T	U	M	H	K
A	I	V	E	L	O	C	I	T	Y
S	L	I	M	P	A	C	T	I	J
S	T	A	T	I	O	N	A	R	Y

C
1. a) When two or more bodies act on each other their total momentum remains constant providing there are no external forces.
   b) It is the velocity given to the gun as a reaction to the shot being ejected from the barrel.
   c) 8 m/s
2. 12 m/s
3. 100 m/s
4. Chemical reactions begin which produce gases. These are ejected out of the rocket pushing it forward.

Pages 100–101   Motion in a circle
A
1. b) 2. c) 3. d) 4. d) 5. a)

B
1.

C	E	N	T	R	I	P	E	T	A	L
E	I	W	A	L	T	Z	E	R	C	D
N	A	R	L	U	S	V	I	N	C	I
T	B	K	C	T	P	E	A	T	E	R
R	C	J	M	L	E	L	R	A	L	E
I	D	I	N	S	E	O	B	N	E	C
F	O	R	C	E	D	C	Z	G	R	T
U	E	H	O	R	V	I	Y	E	A	I
G	R	E	S	U	L	T	A	N	T	O
E	F	G	P	Q	W	Y	X	T	E	N

C
1. a) The speed of the aircraft is constant
   b) The velocity of the aircraft is continually changing
   c) There is a force called the centripetal force being applied to the aircraft which is directed towards the centre of the circle.
   d) She would need to apply a larger force
   e) It would continue to fly in a straight line with the velocity it had at the moment the wire snapped.
2. a) During take off
   b) They are accelerating
   c) They sit in a machine called a centrifuge. They then experience large accelerations by being spun around very quickly in a circle.

Pages 102–103   Static electricity
A
1. d) 2. a) 3. c) 4. d) 5. d)
B
1. a) friction — a method of separating charge
   b) lightning — a phenomenon caused by static electricity
   c) neutral — what an atom will be if it has equal numbers of positive and negative charges
   d) attract — what opposite charges do
   e) nucleus — the centre of an atom
   f) conductor — a material that allows charge to pass through it easily
   g) repel — what similar charges do
   h) proton — positively charged particle
   i) insulator — a material that does not allow charge to pass through it
   j) electron — negatively charged particle
C
1. a) The particles become positively charged.
   b) They are attracted by and stick to the negatively charged plate.
2. a) All the droplets receive a positive charge, so they repel each other and remain as a fine spray.
   b) Less paint is wasted. Even awkward spots get a good coat of paint.
   c) Photocopier.
3. As the fuel passes along a pipe, charges are separated. Without the connection there is the danger of a spark, which may then cause an explosion.
4. As the two insulators are rubbed together, electrons are transferred. The insulator that gains electrons becomes negatively charged. The insulator that loses electrons becomes positively charged.

Pages 104–105   Circuits, currents and resistance
A
1. d) 2. c) 3. d) 4. d) 5. b)
B
1. a) i) 5 V
      ii) 4.4 V
      iii) 4 V
   b) i) 240 Ω
      ii) 300 Ω
      iii) 150 Ω
C
1. a) the same
   b) the same
   c) Both bulbs cease to glow as the series circuit is now incomplete
2. a) 0.4 A
   b) 4.4 V
   c) It continues to glow
   d) stereo systems, electric cookers. It is possible to turn just part of these appliances on or off.

Pages 106–107   Domestic electricity
A
1. d) 2. a) 3. b) 4. c) 5. b)
B
1. a) The earth wire is green and yellow and is connected to the top pin. The live wire is brown and connected to the pin on the right. The neutral wire is blue and connected to the pin on the left.
   b) Fuse
   c) metal/good conductor/brass
   d) The voltage of the mains supply is much higher than that of a cell or battery and is therefore much more dangerous. It is important therefore that connections in mains circuits are made using insulated plugs.
C
1. a) If the user touches the metal casing of kettle A he may complete the circuit and current may flow through him.
   b) If the outer casing is made of plastic current can not flow through it from the heating element. So the user is safe from receiving a shock even if there is no earth wire.
   c) double insulation
2. a) If a fault develops in a circuit and too large a current passes through the fuse the wire melts making the circuit incomplete and so turning it off. The fuse therefore protects the user and limits any damage caused to the appliance by the excessively large current.
   b) 1 A, 3 A, 5 A and 13 A
   c) A kind of fuse which causes a break in a circuit when too much current flows.
   d) A circuit breaker can usually be reset by pressing a button.
   e) When using an electric lawn mower or hedge trimmers.

Pages 108–109   Electrical power
A
1. b) 2. c) 3. b) 4. a) 5. c)
B
1. a) electrical energy, b) forms, c) energy, d) light, e) sound energy (accept also heat), f) power, g) quickly, h) power rating, i) watts
2. a) The bulb is changing 60 J of electrical energy into 60 J of heat and light energy every second.
   b) 1800 J

C

1. a) 13 A
   b) 3 A
   c) 1 A
   d) i) 174 kJ
      ii) 36 kJ
      iii) 3.6 kJ
2. a) 576 000 J or 576 kJ
   b) 90 000 J or 90 kJ

Pages 110–111   The structure of atoms
A

1. c)   2. b)   3. c)   4. d)   5. a)

B

1. a) charge, b) neutral, c) protons,
   d) electrons, e) protons,
   f) nucleus, g) atomic, h) proton
   i) nucleons/particles, j) nucleus,
   k) nucleon, l) atomic mass
2.

THE NUCLEAR ATOM			
Particle	Place	Mass	Relative charge
PROTON	NUCLEUS	1	+1
ELECTRON	orbiting nucleus	0 (1/2000)	–1
NEUTRON	NUCLEUS	1	0

C

1. a) Scientists 'shot' alpha
      particles at a piece of gold leaf
      and then observed how the
      particles were scattered.
   b) Most of an atom is empty
      space.
   c) The mass of an atom is
      concentrated in a very small
      volume and it is positively
      charged.
2. a) 24
   b) 12
   c)

   d) Isotopes are atoms of the
      same element with different
      numbers of neutrons
   e)

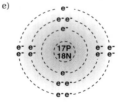

Pages 112–113   Nuclear radiations
A

1. d)   2. a)   3. c)   4. b)   5. a)

B

1. a) false   b) true   c) false
   d) false   e) false   f) true
   g) false   h) true   i) true
   j) false

C

1.

2. Place one source very close to a
   detector eg Geiger-Muller tube.
   Observe count rate. Place piece
   of card between source and tube.
   Observe count rate. If count rate
   has decreased this source must
   be emitting alpha radiation. If
   there is no decrease, the source
   is not emitting alpha radiation.
   Replace the card with a sheet of
   aluminium. Observe the count
   rate. If the count rate has
   decreased now but did not with
   the card this source must be
   emitting beta radiation. Replace
   the aluminium with a thin sheet
   of lead. If the count rate
   decreases even further (maybe
   stops) this confirms the source
   must be emitting gamma
   radiation.
3. a) They have different numbers
      of neutrons (18 and 20)
   b) isotopes
   c) An isotope which emits
      radiation
4. a) An ion is an atom which does
      not have equal numbers of
      protons and electrons.
   b) Alpha particles are bigger and
      heavier.

Pages 114–115   Radioactive decay
A

1. a)   2. d)   3. c)   4. d)   5. d)

B

1. a) $x = 4$ $y = 2$ ^4_2He
   b) $p = 0$ $q = -1$ $^0_{-1}e$
   c) $r = 234$ $s = 90$ $^{234}_{90}Th$
   d) $u = 90$ $v = 39$ $^{90}_{39}Y$

C

1. a) The activity of a source is the
      number of emissions each
      second
   b) After 4 days the number of
      radon 222 nuclei in a sample
      will be halved
   c) 3 days
   d) 1×10^{10}
2. a)

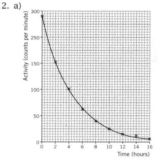

   b) 3 hours
   c) 3-4 counts per minute

Pages 116–117   Uses of radioactivity
A

1. b)   2. a)   3. c)   4. a)   5. d)

B

1. a) alpha radiation, b) air
   particles, c) ions, d) current,
   e) smoke, f) ions, g) current,
   h) smaller, i) sounds.
2. a) The presence and growth of
      bacteria.
   b) If food is exposed to gamma
      radiation the bacteria are
      killed.

C

1. a) gamma
   b) The cancerous cells are killed.
   c) The dose of radiation received
      at B and C is too small to
      damage/kill cells
2. a) oil, gas
   b) a leak in the pipe (possibly a
      blockage)
   c) increase in count rate shown
      by detector (sudden fall in
      detection as tracer cannot
      penetrate blockage)

   d) Alpha and beta radiations
      would be unable to pass
      through soil/earth above pipe.
   e) Avoids the need to dig up
      whole section of pipes to find
      leak/blockage.

Pages 118–119   Nuclear power
A

1. a)   2. d)   3. d)   4. b)   5. c)

B

1. a) These are rods that contain
      the nuclear fuel ie uranium
      235
   b) These rods, made from boron
      or cadmium, control the rate
      of the nuclear reactions by
      absorbing neutrons. The more
      neutrons they absorb the
      slower the nuclear reaction.
   c) Inside the heat exchanger
      heat is transferred from the
      pressurised circulating water
      to cooler water at a lower
      pressure
   d) Steam turns the turbine which
      turns the generator which
      produces the electricity.

C

1. a) In a nuclear fusion reaction
      small nuclei join to make a
      larger nucleus.
   b) The larger nucleus is more
      stable than the smaller nuclei
      from which it was formed.
   c) In stars
2. a) In a nuclear fission reaction a
      large nucleus splits into two
      smaller nuclei.
   b) If uncontrolled the reaction
      will accelerate. The release of
      energy will be so rapid it may
      cause a nuclear explosion.
   c) To slow down the reaction
      some of the neutrons are
      removed ie they are absorbed
      by control rods. To increase
      the rate of reaction the
      control rods are withdrawn so
      that fewer neutrons are
      absorbed.
   d) During fission many parts of
      the nuclear reactor become
      radioactive. All of these parts
      need careful dismantling and
      treatment e.g. storing
      underground.

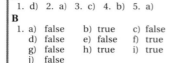

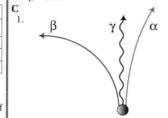

ACKNOWLEDGEMENTS

The author and publisher are grateful to the copyright
holders for permission to use quoted materials and
photographs.

Letts and Lonsdale
4 Grosvenor Place
London SW1X 7DL

School orders: 015395 64910
School enquiries: 015395 65921
Parent and student enquiries: 015395 64913
Email: enquiries@lettsandlonsdale.co.uk
Website: www.lettsandlonsdale.com

First published 2006

Text, design and illustration © 2006 Letts Educational Ltd.

All Rights Reserved. No part of this publication may be
produced, stored in a retrieval system, or transmitted,
in any form or by any means, electronic, mechanical,
photocopying, recording or otherwise, without the
prior permission of Letts Educational Ltd.

British Library Cataloguing in Publication Data.
A CIP record of this book is available from the
British Library.

ISBN: 9781843157137

Book concept and development: Helen Jacobs,
Letts and Lonsdale Publishing Director

Letts editorial team: Catherine Dakin

Series Editor: Brian Arnold

Authors: Brian Arnold, Elaine Gill and Emma Poole

Cover design: Angela English

Inside concept design: Starfish Design

Text design, layout and editorial: MCS Publishing
Services

Letts and Lonsdale make every effort to ensure that all
paper used in our books is made from wood pulp
obtained from well-managed forests, controlled
sources and recycled wood or fibre.

C

1 Marble is a metamorphic rock. Marble contains the compound calcium carbonate.

Calcium carbonate has the formula $CaCO_3$.

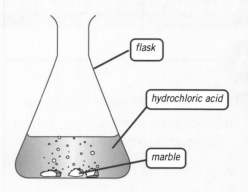

flask

hydrochloric acid

marble

a) Calculate the relative formula mass of calcium carbonate, $CaCO_3$.   (1 mark)

....

b) Marble reacts with hydrochloric acid to produce calcium chloride salt, water and carbon dioxide. Write a word equation for this reaction.
                                                                                    (1 mark)

....

c) The reaction can be summed up by a symbol equation. Balance the equation below to sum up this reaction. You will not need to write in all the spaces shown.   (1 mark)

.....$CaCO_{3(s)}$ + ...$HCl_{(aq)}$ → .....$CaCl_{2(aq)}$ + ...$H_2O_{(l)}$ + ...$CO_{2(g)}$

d) Calculate the mass of carbon dioxide that would be produced when 5 g of calcium carbonate reacts fully with hydrochloric acid.
                                                                                    (2 marks)

....

....

e) Calculate the mass of calcium chloride which would be produced when 5 g of calcium carbonate reacts fully with hydrochloric acid.
                                                                                    (2 marks)

....

....

2 Magnesium carbonate reacts with hydrochloric acid to make magnesium chloride, water and carbon dioxide. The reaction can be summed up by this equation:

magnesium carbonate + hydrochloric acid → magnesium chloride + water + carbon dioxide

$MgCO_3$ + $2HCl$ → $MgCl_2$ + H_2O + CO_2

If 84 g of magnesium chloride is reacted with hydrochloric acid, 18 g of water is made.

Calculate the mass of water made when 21 g of magnesium carbonate reacts fully with hydrochloric acid.
                                                                                    (2 marks)

....

How well did you do?   ✗ 0-10 **Try again**   11-14 **Getting there**   15-19 **Good work**   20-24 **Excellent!** ✓

Reversible reactions

A

1 In a reversible reaction, the forward reaction is exothermic. What can be said about the reverse reaction? **(1 mark)**

a) It is faster. ☐
b) It is an oxidation reaction. ☐
c) It is endothermic. ☐
d) It is more useful. ☐

2 In a reaction, energy in the form of heat is given out. How can this reaction best be described? **(1 mark)**

a) It is fast. ☐
b) It is slow. ☐
c) It is an exothermic reaction. ☐
d) It is an endothermic reaction. ☐

3 In a reaction, energy in the form of heat is taken in. How can this reaction best be described? **(1 mark)**

a) It is fast. ☐
b) It is slow. ☐
c) It is an exothermic reaction. ☐
d) It is an endothermic reaction. ☐

4 In a reversible reaction, three gas molecules join together to form two new gas molecules. If the pressure is increased, what will happen to the yield of the reaction? **(1 mark)**

a) It stays the same. ☐
b) It increases. ☐
c) It decreases. ☐
d) You can only find out by doing the reaction. ☐

5 In a reversible reaction, one gas molecule decomposes to form two new gas molecules. If the pressure is increased, what will happen to the yield of the reaction? **(1 mark)**

a) It stays the same. ☐
b) It increases. ☐
c) It decreases. ☐
d) You can only find out by doing the reaction. ☐

B

1 True or false? True   False   **(5 marks)**

a) In a closed system nothing can escape. ☐ ☐
b) If the temperature increases during an exothermic reversible reaction, the yield of the product also increases. ☐ ☐
c) The burning of methane is an endothermic reaction. ☐ ☐
d) Forward reactions are always exothermic. ☐ ☐
e) Increasing the pressure always increases the yield of a reaction. ☐ ☐

2 In a reversible reaction, A + B ⇌ C, A, B and C are all gases. The forward reaction is exothermic.

Each of the sentences below contains a mistake.
Write down the corrected version of each sentence. **(5 marks)**

a) A and B are the products of the forward reaction. ....

b) The backward reaction is also exothermic. ....

c) Increasing the pressure decreases the yield of the product. ....

d) Increasing the temperature decreases the rate of reaction. ....

e) At equilibrium, all the reactions stop. ....

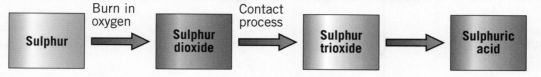

C

1 Sulphuric acid is a very widely used chemical. Sulphuric acid is made from a compound called sulphur trioxide. Sulphur trioxide is made by the Contact process.

| Sulphur | Burn in oxygen → | Sulphur dioxide | Contact process → | Sulphur trioxide | → | Sulphuric acid |

During the Contact process, sulphur dioxide reacts with oxygen to form sulphur trioxide. This reaction can be summed up by the equation below.

Sulphur dioxide + oxygen $\rightleftharpoons$ sulphur trioxide
$$2SO_{2(g)} + O_{2(g)} \rightleftharpoons 2SO_{3(g)}$$

This is an exothermic reaction.

The reaction is carried out in the presence of a vanadium oxide catalyst.

a) i) Name the reactants of the Contact process. (1 mark)

....

  ii) What effect does the vanadium catalyst have on the yield of sulphur trioxide? (1 mark)

....

b) Explain what the symbol $\rightleftharpoons$ means. (1 mark)

....

c) Industrially, this reaction is carried out at 450°C.

  i) State what the effect would be of increasing the temperature on the yield of
     sulphur trioxide. (1 mark)

....

  ii) What is a closed system? (1 mark)

....

Sulphuric Acid

....

The Haber process

A

1 **What is the pressure used in the Haber process?** (1 mark)

a) 100 atmospheres ☐
b) 200 atmospheres ☐
c) 400 atmospheres ☐
d) 450 atmospheres ☐

2 **What is the temperature used in the Haber process?** (1 mark)

a) 150°C ☐
b) 250°C ☐
c) 350°C ☐
d) 450°C ☐

3 **What is the catalyst used in the Haber process?** (1 mark)

a) copper ☐
b) iron ☐
c) nickel ☐
d) vanadium oxide ☐

4 **What does a catalyst do?** (1 mark)

a) increases the temperature ☐
b) increases the pressure ☐
c) increases the rate of the reaction ☐
d) increases the yield ☐

5 **Where does the nitrogen used in the Haber process come from?** (1 mark)

a) natural gas ☐
b) ammonia ☐
c) air ☐
d) volcanoes ☐

B

1 **True or false?**   True False (5 marks)

a) Iron is used as the catalyst in the Haber process. ☐ ☐
b) In industrial terms, 450°C is a very high temperature. ☐ ☐
c) The hydrogen used in the Haber process is obtained from air. ☐ ☐
d) Ammonia is made from hydrogen and oxygen. ☐ ☐
e) Any unreacted nitrogen and hydrogen is released into the environment. ☐ ☐

2 **Complete the following passage.** (10 marks)

Ammonia is a compound made from hydrogen and **a)** .... It has the

b) .... NH_3. Industrially ammonia is made by the **c)** .... process.

Hydrogen is obtained from **d)** .... gas and nitrogen is obtained from the

e) ....

The chemical reaction is an example of a **f)** .... reaction. In the **g)** ....

reaction, the nitrogen and hydrogen react together to form ammonia. In the **h)** ....

reaction, ammonia decomposes to form nitrogen and hydrogen. Ammonia is removed by cooling down

the reaction mixture. The **i)** .... liquefies and can be removed. Any unreacted nitrogen

and hydrogen is **j)** .... to reduce costs.

C

1 Ammonia is made industrially using the Haber process. Ammonia is an important chemical which is used in the manufacture of fertilisers.

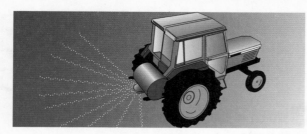

The reaction between hydrogen and nitrogen to make ammonia can be summed up by the equation:

$$N_{2(g)} + 3H_{2(g)} \rightleftharpoons 2NH_{3(g)}$$

The forward reaction is exothermic.

In a closed system, the reaction will eventually reach an equilibrium.

a) What is a closed system?   (1 mark)

....

....

b) What is an equilibrium?   (1 mark)

....

....

c) The process is carried out at a temperature of 450°C. If the temperature is increased, what effect will this have on each of the following?

   i)   the rate of reaction   (1 mark)

   ....

   ii) the yield of this reaction   (1 mark)

   ....

d) The process is carried out at a pressure of 200 atmospheres. If the pressure is increased, what effect will this have on the yield of this reaction?   (1 mark)

....

e) An iron catalyst is used in the industrial production of ammonia. What effect does this catalyst have on each of the following?

   i)   the rate of this reaction   (1 mark)

   ....

   ii) the yield of this reaction   (1 mark)

   ....

2 a) Write a word equation to sum up the reaction between nitrogen and hydrogen to make ammonia.   (1 mark)

....

....

b) Write a balanced symbol equation to sum up this reaction.   (1 mark)

....

....

c) Why is unreacted nitrogen and hydrogen recycled?   (1 mark)

....

....

Rates of reaction

A

1 **What does a catalyst do?** (1 mark)

a) increases the rate of a reaction ☐

b) increases the temperature of
the reaction ☐

c) increases the yield of a reaction ☐

d) increases the time needed for
the reaction ☐

2 **How can the rate of a reaction be
measured?** (1 mark)

a) measure the temperature ☐

b) look at the equation for the reaction ☐

c) reduce the temperature ☐

d) measure how fast the products of the
reaction are made ☐

3 **Which of these will *not* increase the rate of a
reaction?** (1 mark)

a) adding a catalyst ☐

b) decreasing the temperature ☐

c) increasing the surface area ☐

d) increasing the concentration ☐

4 **Which of these will *not* decrease
the rate of a reaction?** (1 mark)

a) adding a catalyst ☐

b) decreasing the temperature ☐

c) decreasing the surface area ☐

d) decreasing the concentration ☐

5 **When is the rate of a reaction
normally fastest?** (1 mark)

a) 0–10s ☐

b) 10–20s ☐

c) 20–30s ☐

d) After the first minute ☐

B

1 George investigated the rate of the reaction between hydrochloric acid and calcium carbonate.
The reaction can be summarised by the following word equation:

> hydrochloric acid + calcium carbonate → calcium chloride + water + carbon dioxide

He recorded the volume of carbon dioxide gas produced every 10 seconds in the table below.

Time (s)	0	10	20	30	40	50	60	70	80	90	100
Volume of gas made (cm³)	0	30	40	50	56	60	60	60	60	60	60

a) **Draw a graph to show George's experiment.** (4 marks)

b) **When is the rate of reaction fastest?** (1 mark)

....

....

c) **When has the reaction finished?** (1 mark)

....

....

C

1 The reaction between magnesium metal and sulphuric acid can be summarised by the word equation:

> magnesium + sulphuric acid → magnesium sulphate + hydrogen

A student wants to investigate the rate of this reaction. She sets up some equipment, which is shown in the diagram below.

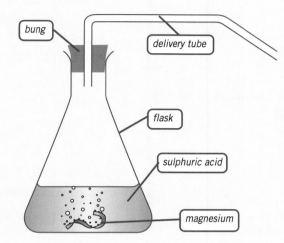

bung

delivery tube

flask

sulphuric acid

magnesium

a) Complete the diagram to show how the amount of hydrogen gas can be measured. **(1 mark)**

b) What other piece of apparatus would the student need to investigate the rate of this reaction? **(1 mark)**

....

c) What measurements should the student take? **(1 mark)**

....

d) The student carries out the reaction at 20°C and 40°C. The student finds that the reaction is faster at the higher temperature. Explain why reactions happen faster at higher temperatures. **(3 marks)**

....

....

....

....

Exothermic and endothermic reactions

A

1 If, overall, a chemical reaction gives out energy, what type of reaction is it? **(1 mark)**

a) catalysed ☐
b) uncatalysed ☐
c) exothermic ☐
d) endothermic ☐

2 If, overall, a chemical reaction takes in energy, what type of reaction is it? **(1 mark)**

a) catalysed ☐
b) uncatalysed ☐
c) exothermic ☐
d) endothermic ☐

3 Methane is the gas burnt in Bunsen burners. Which of these descriptions best describes the reaction that takes place when methane is burnt? **(1 mark)**

a) catalysed ☐
b) slow ☐
c) exothermic ☐
d) endothermic ☐

4 Anhydrous copper sulphate reacts with water to form hydrated copper sulphate. This reaction gives out lots of heat energy. Which of these descriptions best describes the reaction which takes place when anhydrous copper sulphate reacts with water? **(1 mark)**

a) catalysed ☐
b) slow ☐
c) exothermic ☐
d) endothermic ☐

5 Which of the following is a correct statement about bond energy? **(1 mark)**

a) It is the amount of energy required to break one bond. ☐
b) It is the amount of energy required to break one mole of bonds. ☐
c) It is the same for all bonds. ☐
d) It is worked out from the symbol equation for the reaction. ☐

B

1 True or false?   True   False   **(5 marks)**

a) During chemical reactions, some bonds are made and some bonds are broken. ☐ ☐
b) Overall, exothermic reactions take in energy. ☐ ☐
c) During chemical reactions energy is normally given out in the form of electrical energy. ☐ ☐
d) The burning of magnesium is an example of an endothermic reaction. ☐ ☐
e) The thermal decomposition of limestone is an example of an endothermic reaction. ☐ ☐

2 Cross out the incorrect word or phrase to complete these sentences. **(5 marks)**

a) In exothermic reactions, overall, energy is *taken in from the surroundings/given out to the surroundings*.
b) In chemical reactions, bonds are *made and broken/made*.
c) Most exothermic reactions give out *heat energy/sound energy*.
d) The burning of the fuel propane is an *exothermic/endothermic* reaction.
e) Cracking hydrocarbons is an example of an *exothermic/endothermic* reaction.

C

1 Methane is used as a fuel in Bunsen burners.

Fuels are substances that can be burnt to release heat energy. When methane is burnt completely in oxygen, carbon dioxide and water vapour are produced.

The symbol equation for the complete combustion of methane is shown below.

$$CH_4 + 2O_2 \rightarrow CO_2 + 2H_2O$$

a) Write a word equation to summarise this reaction. (1 mark)

....

The diagram below shows the bonds present in molecules of methane, oxygen, carbon dioxide and water.

Bond	Bond energy (kJ mol^{-1})
C–H	413
O=O	498
C=O	805
O–H	464
C–O	358

b) How much energy must be taken in to break the bonds in the methane and water molecules? (1 mark)

....

....

....

....

c) How much energy is given out when the carbon dioxide and water vapour molecules are formed? (1 mark)

....

....

....

....

d) Use your answers to parts b) and c) to prove that the burning of methane is an exothermic reaction. (1 mark)

....

....

....

....

2 Calculate the amount of energy required to break the bonds in one mole of ethanol molecules, C_2H_5OH. (1 mark)

....

....

....

....

How well did you do?   ✗ 0-8 Try again   9-11 Getting there   12-15 Good work   16-20 Excellent!   ✓

Electrolysis of sodium chloride solution

A

1 What is chlorine used to make? (1 mark)

a) salt ☐
b) soap ☐
c) bleach ☐
d) margarine ☐

2 What is hydrogen used to make? (1 mark)

a) salt ☐
b) soap ☐
c) bleach ☐
d) margarine ☐

3 What is sodium hydroxide used to make? (1 mark)

a) salt ☐
b) soap ☐
c) bleach ☐
d) margarine ☐

4 During the electrolysis of sodium chloride, what is the name of the gas released at the positive electrode? (1 mark)

a) sodium hydroxide ☐
b) hydrogen ☐
c) chlorine ☐
d) sodium ☐

5 During the electrolysis of sodium chloride, what is the name of the gas released at the negative electrode? (1 mark)

a) sodium hydroxide ☐
b) hydrogen ☐
c) chlorine ☐
d) sodium ☐

B

1 Use the names in the box to label the diagram. (5 marks)

sodium chloride solution
negative electrode
positive electrode
hydrogen gas
chlorine gas

a)
e)
b)
c)
d)

2 True or false? True False (5 marks)

a) A solution of sodium chloride is called brine. ☐ ☐
b) Hydrogen is made by the manufacture of brine. ☐ ☐
c) Chlorine is used in the manufacture of the plastic PVC. ☐ ☐
d) Sodium is a transition metal. ☐ ☐
e) A chloride ion is a chlorine atom that has gained an electron and has a negative charge. ☐ ☐

C

1 The diagram below shows the electrolysis of concentrated sodium chloride solution.

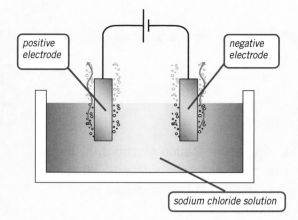

a) **Name the gas produced at the positive electrode.** (1 mark)

....

b) **Give one use of this gas.** (1 mark)

....

c) **Give the symbol equation for the reaction that occurs at the positive electrode.** (1 mark)

....

d) **Name the gas produced at the negative electrode.** (1 mark)

....

e) **Give one use of this gas.** (1 mark)

....

f) **Give the symbol equation for the reaction that occurs at the negative electrode.** (1 mark)

....

g) **Name the other chemical made in this reaction.** (1 mark)

....

h) **Give one use of this chemical.** (1 mark)

....

2 Use the words below to complete the table: (4 marks)

margarine
sodium chloride
chlorine
hydrogen

Word or words	Description
a)	the gas made at the negative electrode during the electrolysis of sodium chloride solution
b)	the chemical name for salt
c)	the gas made at the positive electrode during the electrolysis of sodium chloride solution
d)	a substance made from the reaction between vegetable oils and hydrogen

Acids, bases and neutralisation

A

1 What does the pH of a solution show? (1 mark)

a) its colour ☐
b) its density ☐
c) its smell ☐
d) the concentration of hydrogen ions ☐

2 What is the pH of a strong acid? (1 mark)

a) 1 ☐
b) 7 ☐
c) 6 ☐
d) 14 ☐

3 What is the pH of a neutral solution? (1 mark)

a) 1 ☐
b) 7 ☐
c) 6 ☐
d) 14 ☐

4 What is the pH of a weak alkali? (1 mark)

a) 1 ☐
b) 7 ☐
c) 8 ☐
d) 14 ☐

5 During neutralisation reactions, hydrogen ions react with hydroxide ions. What are the formulae of hydrogen ions and hydroxide ions? (1 mark)

a) H^+ and OH^+ ☐
b) H^+ and OH^- ☐
c) H and OH ☐
d) H^- and OH^+ ☐

B

1 Complete these word equations. (5 marks)

a) acid + alkali → .... + water

b) nitric acid + potassium hydroxide → .... + water

c) potassium hydroxide + sulphuric acid → .... + water

d) calcium hydroxide + hydrochloric acid → .... + water

e) hydrochloric acid + sodium hydroxide → sodium chloride + ...

2 True or false? (5 marks)

	True	False
a) Acids are proton donors.	☐	☐
b) All bases dissolve in water.	☐	☐
c) A base that dissolves in water is called an acid.	☐	☐
d) Strong acids are completely ionised in water.	☐	☐
e) Acidic solutions have a pH greater than 7.	☐	☐

C

1 Indicators are chemicals that can be used to tell whether a solution is acidic, alkaline or neutral by the way they change colour.

Universal Indicator, methyl orange and phenolphthalein are widely used indicators.
The three tables below show the colours of these three indicators in different solutions.

Universal Indicator

pH	Colour
1–2	red
3–5	orange
6	yellow
7	green
8–9	blue
10–14	purple

Methyl orange

pH	Colour
1–3	red
4–14	yellow

Phenolphthalein

pH	Colour
1–9	colourless
10–14	violet

a) What is the colour of the indicator phenolphthalein in a solution of pH 6? (1 mark)

....

b) What is the colour of Universal Indicator in a solution of pH 8? (1 mark)

....

c) What colour is the indicator methyl orange in a pH of 10? (1 mark)

....

d) Which of these indicators could be used to identify a neutral solution? (1 mark)

....

e) What colour would the indicator you have chosen in part d) turn in a neutral solution? (1 mark)

....

f) Which two indicators could be used to differentiate between a strong acid and a weak acid? (1 mark)

....

g) Which two indicators could be used to differentiate between a strong alkali and a weak alkali? (1 mark)

....

How well did you do?   ✗ 0-9 Try again   10-14 Getting there   15-18 Good work   19-22 Excellent! ✓

Making salts

A

1 In which of these applications are salts *not* used in large quantities? **(1 mark)**

a) fireworks
b) fertilisers
c) colouring agents
d) alcoholic drinks

2 Which of these gases is produced when metal carbonates react with acids? **(1 mark)**

a) carbon dioxide
b) hydrogen
c) oxygen
d) ammonia

3 Most metal carbonates are insoluble. How could they best be described? **(1 mark)**

a) acids
b) alkalis
c) bases
d) neutral

4 How is a solid separated from a liquid? **(1 mark)**

a) distillation
b) filtration
c) cracking
d) condensing

5 What are the products of the reaction between copper oxide and sulphuric acid? **(1 mark)**

a) copper sulphate and water
b) copper sulphate and hydrogen
c) copper sulphate
d) copper sulphate and oxygen

B

1 Complete the passage below. **(8 marks)**

When magnesium metal reacts with hydrochloric acid, the salt **a)** .... and the gas **b)** .... are produced. Less **c)** .... metals such as copper do not react directly with acids, so copper salts have to be made in a different way. For example, **d)** .... can be made by reacting copper oxide with sulphuric acid.

Metal carbonates can also be used to make **e)**............................... . The metal carbonate reacts with acid to form salt, **f)** .... and carbon dioxide. When magnesium carbonate reacts with hydrochloric acid, the products are **g)** .... , water and **h)** ....

2 Complete the following word equations involving the formation of salts. **(5 marks)**

a) Zinc + sulphuric acid → zinc sulphate + ...

b) .... + hydrochloric acid → magnesium chloride + hydrogen

c) Copper carbonate + sulphuric acid → .... + water + carbon dioxide

d) Zinc carbonate + nitric acid → zinc nitrate + water + ...

e) Zinc oxide + nitric acid → zinc nitrate + ...

C

1 Place the steps given in the box in order to show how copper chloride is made from copper carbonate and hydrochloric acid. The first one is done for you. (4 marks)

> Copper carbonate is added to the acid until it stops fizzing.

> It is heated until the first crystals appear.

> The solution is poured into an evaporating dish.

> The solution is left for a few days for the copper chloride to crystallise.

> The unreacted copper carbonate is removed by filtering.

a) Copper carbonate is added to the acid until it stops fizzing.

b) ....
....

c) ....
....

d) ....
....

e) ....
....

2 This question is about the reaction between zinc carbonate and hydrochloric acid.

a) Complete the boxes to show the products of the reaction. (1 mark)

Zinc carbonate + hydrochloric acid →

[   ] + [   ] + [   ]

b) What would you see during this reaction? (1 mark)

....

c) How would you know when all of the acid had been used up? (1 mark)

....

d) How would you remove unreacted zinc carbonate? (1 mark)

....

e) How would you get crystals of salt? (1 mark)

....

3 Use the names below to complete the table: (4 marks)

copper chloride
copper sulphate
magnesium nitrate
magnesium chloride

Name	Description
a)	made from magnesium and hydrochloric acid
b)	made from magnesium and nitric acid
c)	made from calcium and sulphuric acid
d)	made from copper carbonate and hydrochloric acid

Chemical tests

A

1 Which gas bleaches damp red litmus paper? (1 mark)

a) oxygen
b) carbon dioxide
c) hydrogen
d) chlorine

2 Which gas relights a glowing splint? (1 mark)

a) oxygen
b) carbon dioxide
c) ammonia
d) chlorine

3 Which gas burns with a squeaky pop? (1 mark)

a) oxygen
b) carbon dioxide
c) hydrogen
d) chlorine

4 Which gas turns limewater cloudy? (1 mark)

a) oxygen
b) carbon dioxide
c) hydrogen
d) chlorine

5 What is the formula for carbon dioxide? (1 mark)

a) O_2
b) CH_4
c) CO_2
d) CO

B

1 Complete the following sentences. (12 marks)

Limewater is used to test for the gas **a)** .... The gas is **b)** .... through limewater. If the limewater turns **c)** ...., the gas is present.

The gas hydrogen is tested for using a **d)** .... splint. If hydrogen is present, it will burn with a **e)** ....

The gas **f)** .... is needed for things to burn. Things burn more brightly in pure oxygen than they do in **g)** .... If a **h)** .... splint is placed in a test tube containing oxygen, the splint **i)** ....

The gas ammonia is tested for using damp, red litmus paper. If this gas is present, the litmus paper changes colour from red to blue.

The **j)** .... chlorine is tested for using **k)** .... red litmus paper. If chlorine is present, the litmus paper is **l)** ....

C

1 This diagram shows the equipment that is used to turn sugar into alcohol and carbon dioxide.

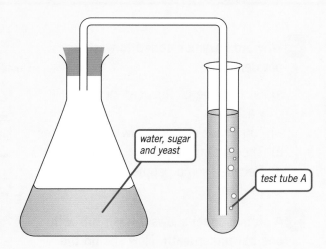

water, sugar and yeast

test tube A

a) Write a word equation for this chemical reaction. **(1 mark)**

....

....

b) i) What should be added to test tube A to test that carbon dioxide has been made? **(1 mark)**

....

....

ii) What would you expect to see happen to the solution in test tube A if carbon dioxide is being made? **(1 mark)**

....

....

2 Use the words below to complete the table: **(4 marks)**

oxygen
carbon dioxide
limewater
chlorine

Name	Description
a)	can be used to test for the presence of carbon dioxide
b)	turns limewater cloudy
c)	things burn better in this gas
d)	bleaches damp red litmus paper

3

3 A student carries out an experiment on an unknown compound.

The compound is a bright pink colour. This means that the compound contains the transition metal cobalt. The student believes that the compound could be cobalt chloride. When cobalt chloride is heated fiercely, it gives off the gas chlorine. Explain how the student should test the gas given off when the compound is heated to see if it is chlorine.

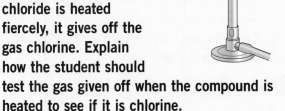

(2 marks)

....

....

Water

A

1 **What can cause eutrophication?** (1 mark)

a) algae ☐
b) nitrate fertilisers ☐
c) fish ☐
d) pesticides ☐

2 **What is added to water to kill microorganisms?** (1 mark)

a) bromine ☐
b) chlorine ☐
c) bacteria ☐
d) fluorine ☐

3 **Which of these ingredients is *not* found in washing powder?** (1 mark)

a) dirt ☐
b) water softener ☐
c) bleach ☐
d) detergent ☐

4 **Why are enzymes added to washing powders?** (1 mark)

a) So that the clothes can be boil washed. ☐
b) To remove stains at low temperatures. ☐
c) They are mentioned in advertisements. ☐
d) Because some people are sensitive to them. ☐

5 **A clothes label shows a wash tub with one bar underneath. How should the item be washed?** (1 mark)

a) wool wash ☐
b) hand wash ☐
c) delicates wash ☐
d) cotton wash ☐

B

1 **True or false?** True False (5 marks)

a) Dry cleaning involves the use of water. ☐ ☐
b) A detergent is used to get rid of dirt. ☐ ☐
c) High levels of dissolved salts in water are very good for people's health. ☐ ☐
d) Aquifers contain water. ☐ ☐
e) Dry cleaning can be used for fabrics that would be damaged by normal washing. ☐ ☐

2 **Complete the following passage.** (8 marks)

Water is an extremely important resource. Around 80% of your body is made from **a)** ....

Although most of our **b)** .... is covered by water most of this water is found in seas

and **c)** .... This water contains very high levels of dissolved **d)** .... so

we cannot drink it.

In the United Kingdom water is only removed from selected sources which have not been

e) ....

Water is taken from lakes, rivers, aquifers and **f)** ....

First the water is **g)** .... to remove solid impurities. Then **h)** .... is

added to kill most of the microorganisms in the water.

C

1 This question is about the ingredients in washing powders.

Use the words below to complete the table. (4 marks)

bleach
optical brighteners
water softener
detergent

Word or words	Description
a)	removes stains
b)	removes the hardness in water so that the detergent can work properly
c)	these molecules have a hydrophylic part and a hydrophobic part
d)	make clothes look very clean

2 Dry cleaning can be used to remove stains that do not dissolve in water.

a) Write down another reason why an item of clothing might be dry cleaned. (1 mark)

....

b) Describe the three steps involved in dry cleaning clothes. (3 marks)

Step 1 ....

Step 2 ....

Step 3 ....

c) Explain why some stains do not dissolve in water. Your answer should include information about the forces of attraction between water molecules and between stain molecules. (2 marks)

....

....

d) Explain why some stains do dissolve in the solvents used in dry cleaning. Your answer should include information about the forces of attraction between the solvent molecules used in dry cleaning and between stain molecules. (2 marks)

....

....

How well did you do? ✗ 0-11 Try again   12-19 Getting there   20-26 Good work   27-30 Excellent! ✓

Uses of oil and alcohol

A

1 Which vitamins can we get from plant oils?

(1 mark)

a) C and A ☐
b) A and D ☐
c) C and B ☐
d) A and K ☐

2 Oils can be extracted from plants. Which of these parts of plants are least likely to yield oils?

(1 mark)

a) fruits ☐
b) stalks ☐
c) seeds ☐
d) nuts ☐

3 Which of these ways of cooking potatoes would you expect to produce food which has the highest energy content?

(1 mark)

a) baking ☐
b) boiling ☐
c) frying ☐
d) microwaving ☐

4 Which of these foods contains plant oil?

(1 mark)

a) bacon ☐
b) olive oil ☐
c) cream ☐
d) butter ☐

5 What is the catalyst used in the hydrogenation of plant oils?

(1 mark)

a) nickel ☐
b) platinum ☐
c) gold ☐
d) sodium ☐

B

1 True or false?

	True	False
a) Traditionally, alcohol has been made by fermentation.	☐	☐
b) Ethene is a member of the alkane family.	☐	☐
c) Hydrochloric acid is used as a catalyst in the industrial manufacture of alcohol.	☐	☐
d) Ethene is reacted with steam to produce ethanol.	☐	☐
e) Ethene is produced by the fractional distillation of crude oil.	☐	☐

(5 marks)

2 Complete the passage below.

(10 marks)

Animal fats are usually **a)** .... at room temperature. Animal fats do not contain any C=C double **b)** .... These are called **c)** .... fats. Scientists believe that if people eat lots of saturated fats it may lead to raised **d)** .... levels.

Vegetable fats are usually **e)** .... at room temperature and they are called

f) .... Vegetable oils contain C=C double **g)** .... These are called

h) .... fats.

Vegetable oils can be made into solids at room temperature by a process known as

i) .... Solid fats are easier to spread and can be used to make products like

j) .... and pastries.

C

1 This label was taken from the side of a tub of low fat spread.

> **Ingredients:**
> Vegetable oils, hydrogenated vegetable oils, water, salt, emulsifier, preservative, colours, Vitamins A and D.

a) **From which two parts of a plant can vegetable oil be extracted?** (2 marks)

roots ☐
seeds ☐
leaves ☐
nuts ☐
flowers ☐

b) **Why should people be careful about the amount of fat that they eat?** (1 mark)

....

....

....

Vegetable oil is liquid

Butter is solid

Golden sunflower oil
the healthy option for all your family 0.5l

BUTTER 200g
BUTTER 200g

c) **Animal fats are usually solid at room temperature. Vegetable fats are usually liquid at room temperature.**

i) **What type of bond is present in vegetable fats that means that they are liquid at room temperature?** (1 mark)

....

ii) **What would you add to test for the presence of this bond?** (1 mark)

....

....

....

iii) **What would you see?** (1 mark)

....

....

....

2 Use the words to complete the table. (4 marks)

unsaturated
covalent
nickel
liquid

Word	Description
a)	state of vegetable oil at room temperature
b)	the catalyst used in the manufacture of margarine
c)	the type of chemical bonds found in fats and oils
d)	the type of covalent bond found in vegetable oils

Speed, velocity and acceleration

A

1 What is the average speed of an athlete who runs 400 m in 80 s? (1 mark)

a) 8 m/s
b) 6 m/s
c) 5 m/s
d) 5 km/h

2 How far will a train travel if it moves at an average speed of 120 km/h for 5 h? (1 mark)

a) 60 km
b) 240 km
c) 600 km
d) 720 km

3 How long will it take a cyclist to travel a distance of 96 km at a speed of 12 km/h? (1 mark)

a) 10.8 h
b) 6 h
c) 10 h
d) 8 h

4 What is the acceleration of a car that increases its speed from 10 m/s to 130 m/s in 6 s? (1 mark)

a) 2 m/s^2
b) 60 m/s^2
c) 6 m/s^2
d) 20 m/s^2

5 Calculate the time it would take for a train to increase its speed from 5 m/s to 45 m/s if its average acceleration during this time is 2.5 m/s^2. (1 mark)

a) 16 s
b) 18 s
c) 25 s
d) 60 s

B

1 a) Explain the difference between the speed of an object and its velocity. (2 marks)

....

b) Give one example of a speed. (1 mark)

....

c) Give one example of a velocity. (1 mark)

....

d) Write down the word equation that relates the speed of an object to the distance it has travelled and the time it has taken. (1 mark)

....

e) Calculate the speed of a train that travels 240 km in 3 hours. (1 mark)

....

f) How far will the train in e) travel in 15 minutes? (1 mark)

....

C

1 The diagram below shows an aircraft waiting to begin take-off from its home airport.

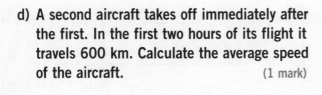

a) Calculate the acceleration of the aircraft if it increases its speed from 0 km/h to 200 km/h in 20 s.   (3 marks)

....

....

....

b) Calculate the distance travelled by the aircraft if it now flies for 4 hours at an average speed of 250 km/h.   (2 marks)

....

....

c) Calculate how long it will take the aircraft to travel 2250 km assuming it continues at the same speed?   (2 marks)

....

....

d) A second aircraft takes off immediately after the first. In the first two hours of its flight it travels 600 km. Calculate the average speed of the aircraft.   (1 mark)

....

e) The final destination of the first aircraft is 2000 km from its home airport. The final destination of the second aircraft is 2100 km from its home airport. Determine
i) which aircraft will land first and
ii) the time difference between the two landings.   (4 marks)

....

....

....

....

2 A car slows down from 30 m/s to 15 m/s in 3 s.

a) Calculate the deceleration of the car.
          (3 marks)

....

....

b) If the car continued to decelerate at this rate how much longer would it be before it came to rest?   (2 marks)

....

....

c) After coming to rest, the car accelerates at the rate of 4 m/s². For how long must the car accelerate in order to reach a speed of 24 m/s?   (2 marks)

....

....

Graphs of motion

A

1 **What does a horizontal line on a distance–time graph indicate?** (1 mark)

a) an object that is travelling along a flat road ☐

b) an object that is accelerating ☐

c) an object that is travelling at constant speed ☐

d) a stationary object ☐

2 **What does a steep straight line sloping upwards on a distance–time graph indicate?** (1 mark)

a) an object that is travelling up a steep incline ☐

b) an object that is travelling quickly ☐

c) an object that is accelerating ☐

d) an object that is stationary ☐

3 **What does a line sloping gently downwards on a speed–time graph indicate?** (1 mark)

a) an object that is travelling down hill ☐

b) an object that is accelerating ☐

c) an object that is gradually slowing down ☐

d) an object that is travelling at a constant speed ☐

4 **What does a horizontal line on a speed–time graph indicate?** (1 mark)

a) an object that is moving with a constant speed ☐

b) an object that is accelerating ☐

c) an object that is travelling along a flat road ☐

d) an object that is decelerating ☐

5 **What does the area under a speed–time graph tell us?** (1 mark)

a) the total distance an object has travelled ☐

b) the average speed of the object during its journey ☐

c) the average acceleration of the object during its journey ☐

d) the total time for the journey ☐

B

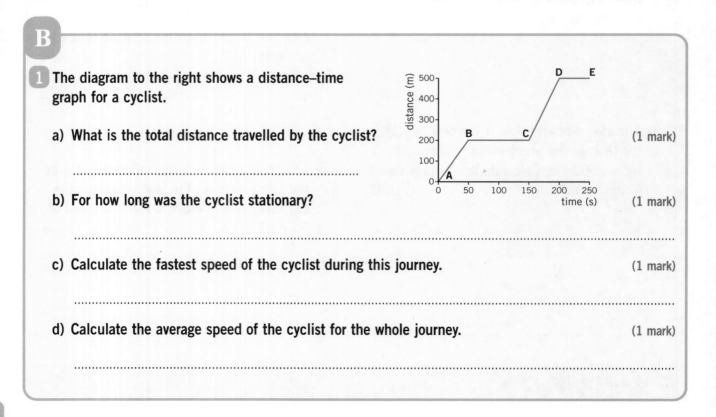

1 **The diagram to the right shows a distance–time graph for a cyclist.**

a) **What is the total distance travelled by the cyclist?** (1 mark)

....

b) **For how long was the cyclist stationary?** (1 mark)

....

c) **Calculate the fastest speed of the cyclist during this journey.** (1 mark)

....

d) **Calculate the average speed of the cyclist for the whole journey.** (1 mark)

....

1 The table below shows how the velocity of an aircraft varied with time.

Time (s)	Velocity (km/h)
0	0
30	90
60	180
90	210
120	240
150	270
180	270
210	270
240	200
270	130
300	130
330	130

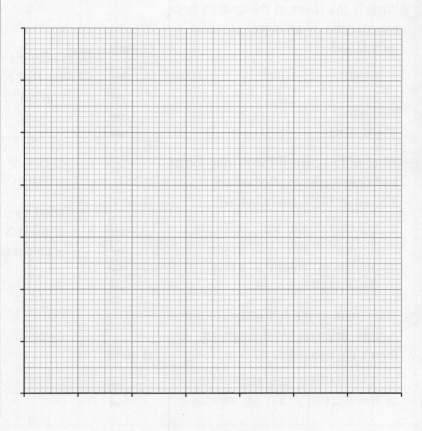

a) Draw a velocity–time graph for this journey. (5 marks)

b) Describe in words the journey of the aircraft. (4 marks)

....

....

....

....

....

c) Calculate the distance travelled by the aircraft between 150 s and 210 s. (2 marks)

....

....

d) Calculate the initial acceleration of the aircraft. (2 marks)

....

....

Balanced and unbalanced forces

A

1 What is the name of the upward force experienced by an object standing on a table? **(1 mark)**

a) weight ☐
b) reaction ☐
c) drag ☐
d) viscosity ☐

2 What will happen if the driving forces and drag forces exerted on an aircraft in flight are balanced? **(1 mark)**

a) the aircraft will stop ☐
b) the aircraft will fly at a constant height ☐
c) the aircraft will fly at a constant speed ☐
d) the aircraft will stall ☐

3 Which one of the following will *not* happen to an object if balanced forces are applied to it? **(1 mark)**

a) it will remain stationary ☐
b) it will travel at a constant speed ☐
c) it will travel in a straight line ☐
d) it will change direction ☐

4 Calculate the acceleration of a 400 kg car that has a force of 1200 N applied to it. **(1 mark)**

a) 30 m/s^2 ☐
b) 480 000 m/s^2 ☐
c) 3 m/s^2 ☐
d) 48 m/s^2 ☐

5 What force must be applied to a rock of mass 5 kg in order to give it an acceleration of 15 m/s^2? **(1 mark)**

a) 3 N ☐
b) 75 N ☐
c) 0.3 N ☐
d) 60 N ☐

B

1 a) Calculate the acceleration of the object in the following situations.

   i) A force of 20 N is applied to a mass of 8 kg. **(2 marks)**

   ii) A force of 5 kN is applied to a mass of 20 kg. **(2 marks)**

   iii) A force of 0.2 kN is applied to a mass of 500 g. **(2 marks)**

  b) Calculate the force being applied to the object in the following situations.

   i) A mass of 5 kg that has an acceleration of 5 m/s^2. **(2 marks)**

   ii) A mass of 15 kg that has an acceleration of 3 m/s^2. **(2 marks)**

C

1 The diagram below shows a beaker floating in water.

A force we call an upthrust is acting on the beaker.

a) Name one other force that is acting on the beaker. (1 mark)

....

b) Indicate the directions of both of these forces on the diagram above. (2 marks)

c) Are these forces balanced or unbalanced? Give reasons for your answer. (2 marks)

....

....

....

d) A small block of iron is placed inside the beaker. The beaker does *not* sink. Explain what happens to the beaker and the forces being applied to it. (3 marks)

....

....

....

....

....

e) A much heavier block of iron is placed inside the beaker. Explain why the beaker sinks. (2 marks)

....

....

....

....

2 An aircraft has a mass of 20 000 kg. Its engines produce a total propulsive force of 100 kN at take-off.

a) Calculate the average acceleration of the aircraft as it travels down the runway. (2 marks)

....

....

....

b) Calculate the 'take-off' speed of the aircraft if it travels down the runway for 15 s before becoming airborne. (3 marks)

....

....

....

....

A

1 **Which of the following conditions causes an object to move at its terminal velocity?** (1 mark)

a) the frictional forces are zero ☐
b) the drag forces and the frictional forces are equal ☐
c) the accelerating forces and the drag forces are equal ☐
d) the accelerating forces are greater than the drag forces ☐

2 **Which of the following will decrease the drag forces experienced by a car?** (1 mark)

a) having a more powerful engine ☐
b) accelerating ☐
c) driving at a constant speed ☐
d) driving more slowly ☐

3 **Which of the following changes will give a car a higher terminal velocity?** (1 mark)

a) tyres with thicker treads ☐
b) a lighter body ☐
c) a more streamlined shape ☐
d) a wider body ☐

4 **Which of the following statements is correct when a parachutist falls at her terminal velocity?** (1 mark)

a) her mass is equal to her drag ☐
b) her weight is equal to her mass ☐
c) her weight is equal to the air resistance ☐
d) air resistance is greater than her weight ☐

5 **A man has a mass of 65 kg. What is his approximate weight on Earth? (g = 10 N/kg)** (1 mark)

a) 650 N ☐
b) 650 J ☐
c) 65 N ☐
d) 130 N ☐

B

1 Below are descriptions of the actions of a skydiver. The results of these actions are also given but they are in the wrong order.

Draw lines connecting the action of the skydiver with the correct result. Then number the actions so that they are in the correct order. (12 marks)

	Action		Result
a)	Skydiver opens parachute	i)	The ground provides an upward force bringing him to a halt
b)	Skydiver lands on feet	ii)	His air resistance suddenly increases and he slows down rapidly
c)	Skydiver begins to free fall	iii)	He begins to accelerate downwards due to the force of gravity
d)	Skydiver continues to fall with parachute open	iv)	His speed increases, his air resistance increases so his acceleration decreases
e)	Skydiver jumps from plane	v)	Forces become balanced so he falls at a constant velocity
f)	Skydiver still free falling	vi)	Forces become balanced again and he falls at a lower terminal velocity

C

1 When a cyclist sits upright and travels along a horizontal road, she travels at a constant speed.

When she leans forward over her handle bars and pedals at the same rate, she accelerates for a while and then again travels at a constant speed.

a) Explain why this happens. (4 marks)

....

....

....

....

....

....

b) Apart from leaning over their handle bars and pedalling harder, suggest two ways in which the four members of a cycling team could increase their top speed. (2 marks)

....

....

....

....

2 A car of mass 500 kg has an engine that produces a propulsive force of 2500 N.

a) Calculate the weight of the car if the Earth's gravitational field strength is 10 N/kg. (2 marks)

....

....

b) Calculate the acceleration of the car as it starts from rest. (2 marks)

....

....

c) Explain why the acceleration of the car decreases as its speed increases. (2 marks)

....

....

d) The car reaches a top speed of 160 km/h. Explain why it is unable to travel at a higher speed by comparing forces now acting on it. (1 mark)

....

....

....

e) Suggest two ways in which the car could be changed so that it could achieve a higher top speed. (2 marks)

....

....

....

Stopping distance

A

1 **Which two distances make up the total stopping distance of a car?** (1 mark)

a) reacting distance and thinking distance ☐
b) braking distance and reaction time ☐
c) braking distance and thinking distance ☐
d) thinking distance and braking force ☐

2 **Which of the following will not affect the braking distance of a car?** (1 mark)

a) the frictional forces between the tyres and the road ☐
b) the mass of the car ☐
c) the speed of the car ☐
d) the reactions of the driver ☐

3 **Which of the following will not affect the thinking distance of a car driver?** (1 mark)

a) the speed of the car ☐
b) the visibility ☐
c) the reactions of the driver ☐
d) the mass of the car ☐

4 **Which factor affects braking distance far more than most people realise?** (1 mark)

a) the mass of the car ☐
b) the speed of the car ☐
c) the size of the engine in the car ☐
d) the reaction time of the driver ☐

5 **If a driver doubles his speed, what will happen to his braking distance?** (1 mark)

a) it will double ☐
b) it will treble ☐
c) it will quadruple ☐
d) it will stay the same ☐

B

1 **Solve as many of these anagrams as you can.** (10 marks)

a) kbgrain ....
b) efcor ....
c) ocreatin ....
d) ireednsst ....
e) vylisibiit ....
f) hiceelv ....
g) sasm ....
h) dsepe ....
i) roficint ....
j) styer ....

2 **Describe three factors that are likely to affect the reaction time of a driver.** (3 marks)

....

....

....

C

1 Brian is taking his family out for a drive in their car.

a) Explain how each of the following will affect the braking distance of the car.

   i)   the mass of the car   (1 mark)

....

....

   ii) the speed of the car   (1 mark)

....

....

   iii) the condition of the road surface

                                               (1 mark)

....

....

....

   iv) the condition of the car's tyres   (1 mark)

....

....

....

b) Explain how each of the following will affect Brian's thinking distance if he has to brake suddenly.

   i)   the speed of the car   (1 mark)

....

....

   ii) the visibility   (1 mark)

....

....

   iii) Brian's reaction time   (1 mark)

....

....

c) Explain how each of the following will affect Brian's reaction time.

   i)   his age   (1 mark)

....

....

   ii) having noisy passengers in his car

                                              (1 mark)

....

....

   iii) having a good night's sleep before he begins a long journey   (1 mark)

....

....

Work and power

A

1 Calculate the work done when a 200 N weight is lifted vertically through a distance of 2 m. (1 mark)

a) 100 J
b) 400 J
c) 1 J
d) 100 kW

2 A man does 400 J of work when he pushes a crate 10 m along the ground. Calculate the size of the force pushing the crate. (1 mark)

a) 25 N
b) 4000 N
c) 0.25 N
d) 40 N

3 A girl pushes a trolley with a force of 25 N. How far must she push the trolley if she is to do 1 kJ of work? (1 mark)

a) 4 m
b) 40 m
c) 25 m
d) 50 m

4 Calculate the power of a machine that does 3 kJ of work in 5 minutes. (1 mark)

a) 10 W
b) 0.6 W
c) 10 kW
d) 60 W

5 A crane has a power rating of 25 kW. Calculate how long it will take the crane to do 10 MJ of work. (1 mark)

a) 400 s
b) 4 s
c) 25 s
d) 250 s

B

1 a) Calculate the work done in each of the following situations.

   i)   A man lifts a box weighing 20 N from the floor and puts it on a shelf 1.5 m high. (2 marks)

   ....

   ii) A lift takes a man weighing 600 N, from the ground floor to the top floor, moving through a distance of 100 m. (2 marks)

   ....

   iii) A crane lifts a steel girder weighing 3000 N through a vertical distance of 30 m. (2 marks)

   ....

   b) Calculate the power of the lift and the crane described above if the time it took to lift each of their loads was 20 s.

   i)   lift   .... (2 marks)

   ii) crane   .... (2 marks)

C

1 A girl weighing 400 N climbs a flight of stairs that is 15 m high.

a) How much work does the girl do in climbing the stairs? **(2 marks)**

....

....

....

b) Calculate the power of the girl if she took 20 s to climb the stairs. **(2 marks)**

....

....

....

2 The lifting motor of a crane has a power rating of 2 kW.

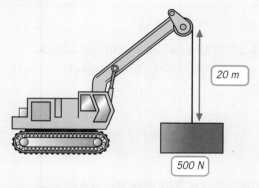

20 m

500 N

a) Calculate the work done when a crane lifts a wooden beam weighing 500 N to a height of 20 m. **(2 marks)**

....

....

....

b) Calculate how long it will take to lift the wooden beam to this height. **(2 marks)**

....

....

....

3 A lift is driven by a motor that has a power rating of 2 kW. Assuming that the motor is 100% efficient and that friction can be ignored, how long will it take for the lift to travel 20 m upwards if the lift and its load weigh 5 kN? **(3 marks)**

....

....

....

....

Kinetic energy and potential energy

A

1 Which of the following will not affect the potential energy of an object? (1 mark)

a) its mass ☐
b) its speed ☐
c) its height above the ground ☐
d) the gravitational field strength ☐

2 Which of the following will not affect the kinetic energy of an object? (1 mark)

a) its mass ☐
b) its speed ☐
c) its velocity ☐
d) its height above the ground ☐

3 Calculate the weight of an object that has a mass of 15 kg. (g = 10 N/kg) (1 mark)

a) 150 N ☐
b) 1.5 N ☐
c) 0.66 N ☐
d) 1.5 J ☐

4 Which of the following statements about potential energy is true when an object is falling at its terminal velocity? (1 mark)

a) the potential energy is making it fall ☐
b) the potential energy is being used to do work against friction ☐
c) the potential energy is being changed into kinetic energy ☐
d) the potential energy is constant ☐

5 Why do cars that travel around a roller coaster gradually climb smaller and smaller hills? (1 mark)

a) because they are gradually losing energy ☐
b) because they are coming to the end of the ride ☐
c) because there is more friction ☐
d) because the cars are getting heavier ☐

B

1 Calculate the kinetic energy of the following objects.

a) a man of mass 80 kg running at 10 m/s .... (2 marks)

b) a car of mass 500 kg travelling at 30 m/s .... (2 marks)

c) an aircraft of mass 10 000 kg travelling at 200 m/s .... (2 marks)

2 Calculate the potential energy of the following objects. (g = 10 N/kg)

a) a crate of mass 100 kg suspended 10 m above the ground (2 marks)

....

b) a hiker of mass 60 kg at the top of a mountain 3000 m high (2 marks)

....

c) an arrow of mass 100 g that is 50 m above the ground at the top of its flight (2 marks)

....

C

1 The diagram below shows what happens to a steel ball after it has been dropped onto a concrete floor.

a) What kind of energy does the ball possess before it is dropped? (1 mark)

....

b) If the ball has a mass of 200 g and is dropped from a height of 2 m, calculate the energy the ball possesses. (g = 10 N/kg) (2 marks)

....

....

c) What happens to this energy as the ball falls? (1 mark)

....

d) Calculate the speed of the ball just before it hits the floor for the first time. (3 marks)

....

....

....

e) Describe the energy change that is taking place *after* the ball has hit the floor. (1 mark)

....

....

....

f) Explain why the ball is unable to bounce back up to the position from which it was first released. (1 mark)

....

....

....

g) If the ball is now dropped from a height of 1 m, how would the behaviour of the ball be different from when it was dropped from 2 m? (2 marks)

....

....

....

....

h) If the steel ball was replaced with a table tennis ball, how would this affect the energy changes that take place after the ball is dropped? (3 marks)

....

....

....

Momentum

A

1 **Which of the following are multiplied to calculate the momentum of an object?** (1 mark)

a) mass and acceleration

b) distance and acceleration

c) mass and velocity

d) force and distance

2 **What are the units of momentum?** (1 mark)

a) m/s

b) m/s^2

c) kg m/s

d) kg m/s^2

3 **Calculate the momentum of a car of mass 800 kg that is moving with a velocity of 20 m/s.** (1 mark)

a) 320 000 kg m/s

b) 16 000 kg m/s

c) 320 000 kg m/s^2

d) 16 000 kg m/s^2

4 **Which of the following statements about momentum is true?** (1 mark)

a) momentum is a force

b) momentum is a vector

c) momentum is a speed

d) momentum is a velocity

5 **Which of the following does not change the momentum of an object?** (1 mark)

a) changing its speed

b) changing its direction

c) changing its velocity

d) changing its temperature

B

1 Calculate the momentum of each of the following objects.

a) a car of mass 500 kg moving at a speed of 30 m/s .... (1 mark)

b) an athlete of mass 60 kg moving at a speed of 10 m/s .... (1 mark)

2 Calculate the masses of the following.

a) a bus moving at 15 m/s with a momentum of 30 000 kg m/s .... (1 mark)

b) a horse moving at 20 m/s with a momentum of 8000 kg m/s .... (1 mark)

3 Calculate the velocities of the following objects.

a) an aircraft with a mass of 10 000 kg and a momentum of 200 000 kg m/s (1 mark)

....

b) a motor bike with a mass of 200 kg and a momentum of 8000 kg m/s (1 mark)

....

C

1 The picture below shows a car that has been used to test passenger safety features.

a) What is a car's crumple zone? **(2 marks)**

....

....

....

....

....

....

b) How does a crumple zone increase passenger safety during a crash? **(2 marks)**

....

....

....

....

....

c) Name two other car safety features found in many cars that help increase the survivability of passengers during a crash.

(2 marks)

....

....

d) Select one of these features and explain how it works using the following equation.

(2 marks)

$$\text{force} = \frac{\text{change in momentum}}{\text{time taken for change}}$$

....

....

....

....

e) A man of mass 80 kg is travelling in a car at 30 m/s. Calculate his momentum.

(2 marks)

....

....

f) The car is involved in a collision. The car and the man are brought to rest in 0.5 s. Calculate the force exerted on the man during this deceleration. **(2 marks)**

....

....

....

....

How well did you do?   ✗ 0-10 **Try again**   11-15 **Getting there**   16-19 **Good work**   20-23 **Excellent!** ✓

Collisions and explosions

A

1 As long as there are no external forces when two bodies collide, which of the following statements is true? **(1 mark)**

a) Their total velocities before and after the collision are the same. ☐

b) Their total momentums before and after the collision are the same. ☐

c) Their total momentums after the collision will be less if there is loss of energy. ☐

d) They will always move in the same direction after the collision. ☐

2 The total momentum of two cars before they collide is 20 000 kg m/s. Assuming there are no external forces, if one of the cars has a mass that is twice the other, which of the following statements is true? **(1 mark)**

a) The velocity of the larger car will be greater than the velocity of the smaller car. ☐

b) The total momentum of the two cars will be unchanged. ☐

c) The total momentum of the two cars will have decreased. ☐

d) Both cars will have a momentum of 10 000 kg m/s. ☐

3 How do rockets move forward? **(1 mark)**

a) by ejecting gases from the back ☐

b) by pushing air behind them ☐

c) by pushing off against the ground ☐

d) by pulling their way through the air ☐

4 Which of the following will reduce the recoil from a gun? **(1 mark)**

a) decreasing the mass of the gun ☐

b) increasing the mass of the shot ejected from the gun ☐

c) reducing the speed with which the shot is ejected ☐

d) increasing the length of the gun barrel ☐

5 A man of mass 80 kg steps off an unsecured rowing boat of mass 160 kg. If the initial velocity of the man is 4 m/s, what is the initial velocity of the rowing boat? **(1 mark)**

a) 2 m/s towards the man ☐

b) 4 m/s towards the man ☐

c) 4 m/s away from the man ☐

d) 2 m/s away from the man ☐

B

1 Find nine words connected with this topic in this word search. **(9 marks)**

A	R	O	C	K	E	T	D	F	M
B	E	X	P	L	O	S	I	O	N
C	C	O	L	L	I	S	I	O	N
M	O	M	E	N	T	U	M	H	K
A	I	V	E	L	O	C	I	T	Y
S	L	I	M	P	A	C	T	I	J
S	T	A	T	I	O	N	A	R	Y

C

1 a) State the Principle of Conservation of Momentum. (2 marks)

....
....
....

b) What is meant by the phrase 'recoil of a gun'? (2 marks)

....
....
....

c) A shot of mass 0.2 kg is ejected from a shotgun with a velocity of 100 m/s. If the mass of the gun is 2.5 kg, calculate its recoil velocity. (3 marks)

....
....
....

2 A ball of mass 0.5 kg travelling at 10 m/s strikes a second stationary ball of mass 0.25 kg.

After the collision, the first ball continues to move in the same direction with a velocity of 4 m/s. Calculate the new velocity of the second ball. (4 marks)

....
....
....
....

3 A bullet of mass 0.05 kg enters a stationary block of wood.

The block and bullet then move with a new velocity of 10 m/s. If the mass of the wood is 0.45 kg, calculate the initial speed of the bullet. (3 marks)

....
....
....

4 The diagram below shows a firework rocket just as it is taking off.

Explain why the rocket takes off several seconds after the touch paper has been lit. (3 marks)

....
....
....
....

Motion in a circle

A

1 **Which statement is true if an object is travelling in a circle?** (1 mark)

a) It is travelling at a constant velocity.
b) It is accelerating.
c) There is no unbalanced force being applied to it.
d) Its average speed is zero.

2 **Which statement is true about the force that causes an object to travel in a circle?** (1 mark)

a) It is called the centrifugal force.
b) It acts in the same direction in which the object is moving.
c) It always acts towards the centre of the circle.
d) It always acts away from the centre of the circle.

3 **A ball on the end of a piece of string is being made to travel around in a horizontal circle. What happens if the string snaps?** (1 mark)

a) The ball will move directly away from the centre of the circle.
b) The ball will move towards the centre of the circle.
c) The ball will stop.
d) The ball will continue with the velocity it had at the moment the string snapped.

4 **Which of the following is moving in a circle?** (1 mark)

a) a ski jumper sliding down a ramp
b) a skater spinning on the spot
c) a rocket travelling to the Moon
d) the Moon travelling around the Earth

5 **What must we do to make an object travel faster in a circle?** (1 mark)

a) apply a bigger centripetal force
b) apply a bigger centrifugal force
c) apply a bigger tangential force
d) give the object more mass

B

1 Eleven words connected with this topic are hidden in this word search.

Can you find them all?

The word search also includes the name of a fairground ride that moves its passengers in a circle ..... as well as spinning them around. Can you find it?

C	E	N	T	R	I	P	E	T	A	L
E	I	W	A	L	T	Z	E	R	C	D
N	A	R	L	U	S	V	I	N	C	I
T	B	K	C	T	P	E	A	T	E	R
R	C	J	M	L	E	L	R	A	L	E
I	D	I	N	S	E	O	B	N	E	C
F	O	R	C	E	D	C	Z	G	R	T
U	E	H	O	R	V	I	Y	E	A	I
G	R	E	S	U	L	T	A	N	T	O
E	F	G	P	Q	W	Y	X	T	E	N

(11 marks)

C

1 The diagram below shows a model aircraft that is flying in circles.

The plane is controlled using the wire held by the girl. It takes 5 s for the aircraft to complete one circle.

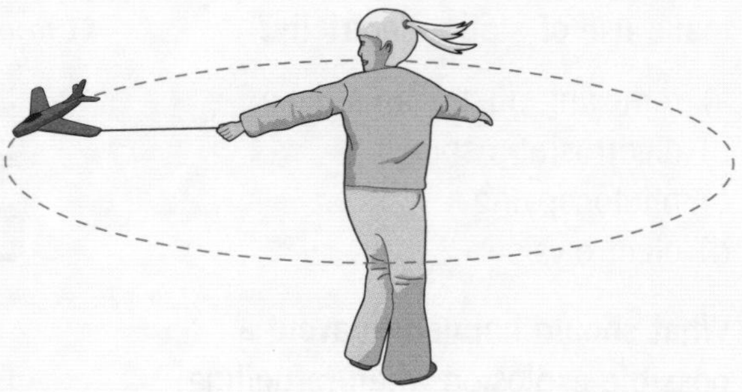

a) Describe the speed of the aircraft. (1 mark)

....

....

b) Describe the velocity of the aircraft. (1 mark)

....

....

c) Describe the force that is being applied to the aircraft. (2 marks)

....

....

d) If the speed of the aircraft was increased but it followed the same path, how would this affect the force the girl would have to apply to it through the wire? (1 mark)

....

....

e) If the control wire snapped, describe what would happen to the aircraft immediately after the break. (2 marks)

....

....

....

....

2 Astronauts train their bodies so that they can withstand large g-forces.

a) When will astronauts experience g-forces? (1 mark)

....

....

b) What is happening to the astronauts that causes these g-forces? (1 mark)

....

....

c) Explain how astronauts train their bodies to withstand these g-forces. (2 marks)

....

....

....

....

....

How well did you do? 0-9 Try again 10-14 Getting there 15-19 Good work 20-27 Excellent!

Static electricity

A

1 **A neutral atom contains equal numbers of which of the following?** (1 mark)

a) electrons and ions ☐
b) electrons and neutrons ☐
c) protons and neutrons ☐
d) protons and electrons ☐

2 **If a neutral object is to become positively charged what must happen?** (1 mark)

a) It must lose electrons ☐
b) It must gain protons ☐
c) It must lose ions ☐
d) It must gain protons and electrons ☐

3 **Which of the following statements is true?** (1 mark)

a) A positive ion will repel an electron. ☐
b) Two negative charges placed close together will attract. ☐
c) Two positive charges placed close together will repel. ☐

d) A negative ion will attract an electron. ☐

4 **Which of the following does not make use of static electricity?** (1 mark)

a) removing dust from smoke ☐
b) electrostatic spraying ☐
c) photocopying ☐
d) electrolysis ☐

5 **What should happen to avoid a possible explosion when refuelling aircraft that have just landed?** (1 mark)

a) The aircraft should be parked in a north-south direction. ☐
b) The aircraft should be insulated. ☐
c) The fuel pipes should be made from a good insulator. ☐
d) The aircraft and refuelling truck should be earthed. ☐

B

1 Rearrange the following anagrams and then draw lines to match them up with their descriptions.

	Anagram	Answer	Description
a)	croniitf		the centre of an atom
b)	ggtliihnn		a method of separating charge
c)	tnaeulr		positively charged particle
d)	caatttr		negatively charged particle
e)	csuunle		a material that allows charge to pass through it easily
f)	ruoontdcc		a material that does not allow charge to pass through it
g)	plree		what similar charges do
h)	tpoonr		what opposite charges do
i)	aouinrslt		a phenomenon caused by static electricity
j)	creetnlo		what an atom will be if it has equal numbers of positive and negative charges

(10 marks)

C

1 The diagram below shows how static electricity can be used to remove dust from smoke.

negatively charged plate

dust particles removed

smoke and dust

positively charged plate

a) What happens to the particles of dust as they pass through the lower plate?
(2 marks)

....

....

b) What happens to these dust particles as they pass through the upper plate?
(2 marks)

....

....

2 The diagram below shows a bicycle frame being painted using electrostatic spraying.

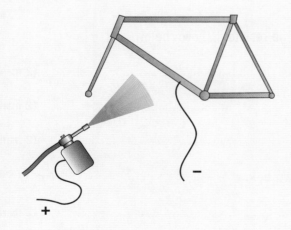

−

+

a) Explain why the paint comes out of the nozzle and forms a fine spray.
(3 marks)

....

....

....

b) Give two advantages of using this method of painting the frame compared with using a spray can.
(2 marks)

....

....

c) Name one piece of office equipment that makes use of static electricity.
(1 mark)

....

3 Explain why it is important that a conductor is connected between an aircraft and a fuel tanker before refuelling begins.
(3 marks)

....

....

....

4 Explain in detail how rubbing two insulators together can produce static electricity. You may draw diagrams if you feel this will help.
(4 marks)

....

....

....

....

Circuits, currents and resistance

A

1 The sum of the voltages across all the components in a series circuit is equal to: (1 mark)

a) the current flowing through the cell or battery ☐

b) the current flowing in the circuit ☐

c) the energy lost by the current in the cell or battery ☐

d) the voltage across the cell or battery ☐

2 Which of the following statements is untrue for a series circuit? (1 mark)

a) current is the same in all parts of the circuit ☐

b) energy is transferred by the components in the circuit ☐

c) current is used up as it flows around the circuit ☐

d) there are no junctions ☐

3 Which of the following is untrue for a parallel circuit? (1 mark)

a) current flowing into a junction equals the current flowing out ☐

b) part of the circuit can be turned on and off ☐

c) current may be different in different parts of the circuit ☐

d) current flowing out of the cell or battery will be larger than the current flowing back into it ☐

4 Currents of 3 A, 4 A and 2 A flow into a junction in a parallel circuit. What will the current flowing out of the junction be? (1 mark)

a) 5.0 A ☐

b) 1.0 A ☐

c) 24 A ☐

d) 9.0 A ☐

5 What units are used to measure the resistance of a component? (1 mark)

a) amps ☐

b) ohms ☐

c) coulombs ☐

d) volts ☐

B

1 a) Calculate the potential difference across each of the resistors shown below.

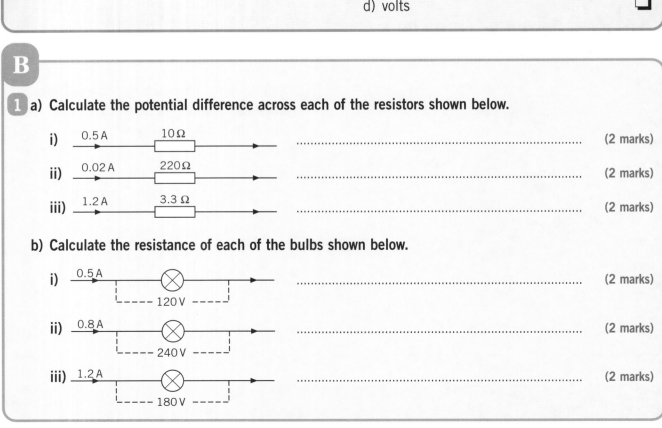

i) 0.5 A   10 Ω .... (2 marks)

ii) 0.02 A   220 Ω .... (2 marks)

iii) 1.2 A   3.3 Ω .... (2 marks)

b) Calculate the resistance of each of the bulbs shown below.

i) 0.5 A   120 V .... (2 marks)

ii) 0.8 A   240 V .... (2 marks)

iii) 1.2 A   180 V .... (2 marks)

1 The reading on ammeter X is 100 mA.

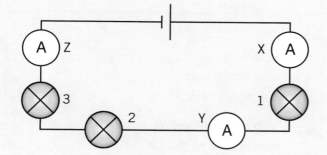

a) Is the reading on ammeter Y greater than, the same as or less than that on ammeter X? (1 mark)

....

b) Is the reading on ammeter Z greater than, the same as or less than that on ammeter Y? (1 mark)

....

c) Bulb 3 develops a fault and breaks. Explain what happens to bulbs 1 and 2. (2 marks)

....

....

....

....

2 Look at the circuit diagram below.

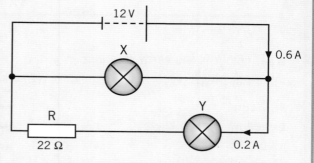

a) What current flows through bulb X in the circuit shown above? (2 marks)

....

....

b) What is the potential difference across the resistor R? (2 marks)

....

....

c) If bulb Y breaks, what happens to bulb X? (1 mark)

....

....

....

d) Name one piece of electrical equipment that contains parallel circuits. Explain why you believe it contains parallel circuits. (3 marks)

....

....

....

Domestic electricity

A

1 **What colour is the earth wire in a three-pin plug?** (1 mark)

a) green ☐
b) yellow ☐
c) brown ☐
d) green and yellow ☐

2 **What is the name of a current that is continuously changing direction?** (1 mark)

a) alternating current ☐
b) alternator current ☐
c) direct current ☐
d) induced current ☐

3 **What is name of the wire through which electrical energy travels to an appliance?** (1 mark)

a) earth wire ☐
b) live wire ☐
c) connecting wire ☐
d) neutral wire ☐

4 **Which of the following is not a common fuse in the UK?** (1 mark)

a) 1 A ☐
b) 3 A ☐
c) 10 A ☐
d) 13 A ☐

5 **What is the approximate voltage from the mains in the UK?** (1 mark)

a) 200 V ☐
b) 230 V ☐
c) 110 V ☐
d) 12 V ☐

B

1 The diagram opposite shows the inside of a three-pin plug.

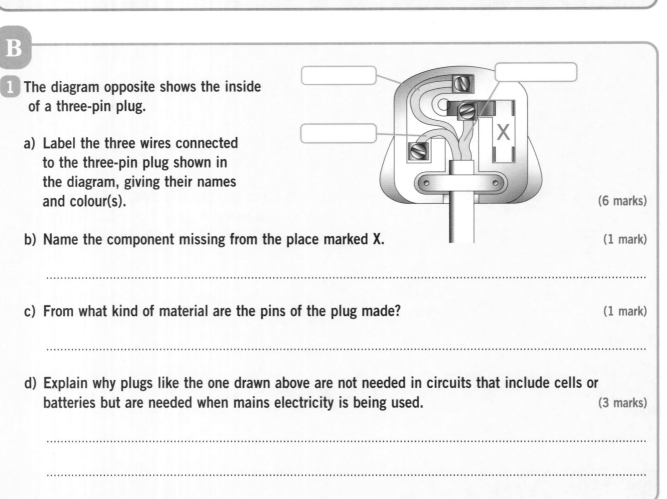

a) Label the three wires connected to the three-pin plug shown in the diagram, giving their names and colour(s). (6 marks)

b) Name the component missing from the place marked X. (1 mark)

....

c) From what kind of material are the pins of the plug made? (1 mark)

....

d) Explain why plugs like the one drawn above are not needed in circuits that include cells or batteries but are needed when mains electricity is being used. (3 marks)

....

....

1 The diagrams below show two types of kettle.

Kettle A has a metal outer casing, and kettle B has a plastic outer casing.

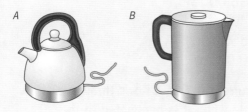

a) Explain why someone using kettle A might receive a shock if the heating element is faulty and there is no earth wire connected. **(2 marks)**

....

....

....

b) Explain why there is no need for an earth wire to be connected to kettle B. **(2 marks)**

....

....

....

c) What is the name of the kind of insulation provided by the plastic casing of kettle B? **(1 mark)**

....

2 The diagram below shows a 13 A cartridge fuse.

a) Explain how this fuse works and why we should include a fuse similar to that shown above in all mains circuits. **(4 marks)**

....

....

....

....

b) Give the values of two fuses commonly used in the UK. **(2 marks)**

....

....

c) What is a circuit breaker? **(1 mark)**

....

....

d) How is a circuit breaker different from a cartridge fuse? **(2 marks)**

....

....

....

e) Give one example of when someone might use a circuit breaker. **(1 mark)**

....

....

How well did you do? ✗ 0-6 **Try again**   7-15 **Getting there**   16-24 **Good work**   25-31 **Excellent!** ✓

Electrical power

A

1 How much electrical energy is changed into heat and light energy when a 100 W light bulb is turned on for 5 minutes? *(1 mark)*

a) 300 J
b) 30 kJ
c) 500 J
d) 3000 J

2 If an electric heater has a power rating of 3 kW it changes: *(1 mark)*

a) 3000 J of electrical energy into heat energy every hour
b) 3 J of electrical energy into heat energy every second
c) 3000 J of electrical energy into heat energy every second
d) 3 kJ of electrical energy into heat energy every minute

3 Calculate the power of a light bulb that transfers 1200 J of electrical energy into heat and light energy in 30 s. *(1 mark)*

a) 36 000 W
b) 40 W
c) 360 W
d) 0.025 W

4 A current of 8.7 A flows through a kettle when it is connected to the mains. Calculate the power of the kettle if the mains voltage is 230 V. *(1 mark)*

a) 2.0 kW
b) 200 W
c) 3.0 kW
d) 3.3 kW

5 For how long must a 100 W bulb be turned on for it to transfer 3 kJ of electrical energy? *(1 mark)*

a) 3000 s
b) 300 s
c) 30 s
d) 33 s

B

1 Complete the following passage. *(9 marks)*

Electrical appliances transfer **a)** .... into other **b)** .... of **c)** ....

For example, a television changes electrical energy into **d)** .... and **e)** ....

The **f)** .... of an appliance is a measure of how **g)** .... the changes take place.

This **h)** .... is measured in **i)** .... or kW.

2 This bulb has a power rating of 60 W.

60 W

a) Explain what the above sentence tells you about the bulb. *(1 mark)*

....

b) Calculate the amount of electrical energy that is converted into heat and light energy when a 60 W bulb is turned on for 30 s. *(3 marks)*

....

C

1 The diagram below shows a cartridge fuse.

The most common fuse ratings in the UK are
1 A, 3 A, 5 A and 13 A.

a) Calculate the fuse needed for a heater rated
   at 230 V 2.9 kW.   (3 marks)

   ....

   ....

   ....

b) Calculate the fuse needed for an electric
   iron rated at 230 V 600 W.   (3 marks)

   ....

   ....

   ....

c) Calculate the fuse needed for a 230 V 60 W
   bulb.   (3 marks)

   ....

   ....

   ....

d) For each of the following appliances,
   calculate how much electrical energy they
   would transfer if they were turned on for
   1 minute.

   i) heater in a)   (2 marks)

   ....

   ....

ii) iron in b)   (2 marks)

   ....

   ....

iii) bulb in c)   (2 marks)

   ....

   ....

2 a) Calculate the amount of electrical energy
        that is converted into other forms when
        a hairdryer rated at 1200 W is used for
        8 minutes.   (3 marks)

   ....

   ....

   ....

b) Calculate the amount of energy that is
   converted into other forms when a radio
   rated at 25 W is turned on for 1 hour.
                                           (3 marks)

   ....

   ....

   ....

The structure of atoms

A

1 Which of the following was not confirmed by the alpha-particle scattering experiment? **(1 mark)**

a) most of an atom is empty space ☐
b) an atom has a very dense central core ☐
c) all objects are made from particles called atoms ☐
d) the centre of an atom is positively charged ☐

2 Which of these is not a particle found in an atom? **(1 mark)**

a) proton ☐
b) krypton ☐
c) neutron ☐
d) electron ☐

3 What are atoms of the same element that have nuclei with different numbers of neutrons called? **(1 mark)**

a) elements ☐
b) isomers ☐
c) isotopes ☐
d) ions ☐

4 Lithium has a nucleon number of 7 and a proton number of 3. Which of the following statements is false? **(1 mark)**

a) the outer orbit of a lithium atom contains just 1 electron ☐
b) its nucleus contains 3 protons ☐
c) an atom of lithium will have 3 electrons orbiting its nucleus ☐
d) its nucleus contains 3 neutrons ☐

5 What is another name for the atomic mass of an atom? **(1 mark)**

a) nucleon number ☐
b) atomic number ☐
c) proton number ☐
d) valency ☐

B

1 Fill in the missing words in the passage below. **(12 marks)**

Atoms have no overall **a)** .... They are **b)** .... This is because they contain equal numbers of **c)** .... and **d)** .... The number of **e)** .... an atom has in its **f)** .... is called the **g)** .... number or the **h)** .... number. The total number of **i)** .... in the **j)** .... of an atom is called the **k)** .... number or the **l)** ....

2 Fill in the missing spaces in the table below. **(9 marks)**

THE NUCLEAR ATOM			
Particle	Place	Mass	Relative charge
			+1
	Orbiting nucleus		
			0

C

1 The diagram below shows the results of the alpha-scattering experiment.

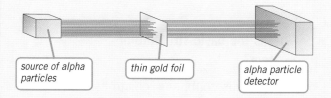

source of alpha particles   *thin gold foil*   *alpha particle detector*

a) Why was this called 'the alpha-scattering experiment'? (2 marks)

....

....

b) Most of the particles passed straight through the thin gold leaf. What did this suggest about the structure of a gold atom? (1 mark)

....

c) A very small number of particles travelled back almost in the direction from which they came. What did this suggest about the structure of a gold atom? (1 mark)

....

2 The diagram below shows the atomic structure of the element magnesium.

a) What is the nucleon number of magnesium? (1 mark)

....

b) What is the proton number of magnesium? (1 mark)

....

c) Sulphur has a nucleon number of 32 and a proton number of 16. Draw, in the space below, the atomic structure of an atom of sulphur. (3 marks)

Chlorine has a proton number of 17. It is an element that has two isotopes. The nucleon numbers of these isotopes are 35 and 37.

d) What are isotopes? (1 mark)

....

e) In the space below, draw the isotopes of chlorine. (4 marks)

Nuclear radiations

A

1 Which of the following statements is true for alpha particles? (1 mark)

a) They travel at the speed of light. ☐
b) They are unaffected by electric fields. ☐
c) They are poor ionisers. ☐
d) They are helium nuclei. ☐

2 Which of the following statements is true for beta particles? (1 mark)

a) They are fast-moving electrons. ☐
b) They are uncharged. ☐
c) They are more penetrating than gamma rays. ☐
d) They are unaffected by magnetic fields. ☐

3 Which of the following statements is true for gamma rays? (1 mark)

a) They are deflected by magnetic fields. ☐
b) They are not very penetrating. ☐
c) They travel at the speed of light. ☐
d) They are deflected by electric fields. ☐

4 What is the basic structure of an atom? (1 mark)

a) a nucleus containing electrons and protons and neutrons in orbit ☐
b) a nucleus containing neutrons and protons and electrons in orbit ☐
c) a nucleus containing electrons and neutrons and protons in orbit ☐
d) a nucleus containing protons and electrons and neutrons in orbit ☐

5 Which of the following statements is untrue? (1 mark)

a) Alpha radiation is the least penetrating radiation and is therefore unlikely to damage living cells. ☐
b) A radioactive substance gives out radiation. ☐
c) A dosimeter monitors exposure to radiation. ☐
d) Thick sheets of a dense metal are needed to stop gamma radiation. ☐

B

1 Which of the following statements are true and which are false?   True   False   (10 marks)

a) Alpha particles are slow-moving, high-penetrating, helium nuclei. ☐ ☐
b) Gamma waves move at the speed of light. ☐ ☐
c) Beta particles are deviated a lot by magnetic and electric fields because they do not move very quickly. ☐ ☐
d) Alpha particles are not deviated much by magnetic and electric fields because they are moving very quickly. ☐ ☐
e) Gamma radiation is very penetrating and therefore produces lots of ions as it passes through objects. ☐ ☐
f) Gamma radiation is uncharged and is therefore not affected by magnetic or electric fields. ☐ ☐
g) Alpha radiation is very similar to X-rays. ☐ ☐
h) Beta particles are more penetrating than alpha particles because they are smaller. ☐ ☐
i) Alpha radiation is unable to travel more than a few centimetres in air. ☐ ☐
j) An ion is an atom that has equal numbers of protons and electrons. ☐ ☐

1 The diagram below shows the effect of a magnetic field on all three types of radiation.

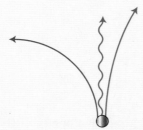

Identify on the diagram which path is followed by which radiation. (3 marks)

2 You are given two radioactive sources.

Both sources emit two types of radiation. It is thought that one of the sources is emitting alpha and gamma radiation and the other beta and gamma radiation.

Describe an experiment you would carry out to discover which types of radiation each source was emitting. (You can assume that there is no background radiation.) (5 marks)

....

....

....

....

....

....

....

....

....

3 The diagrams below show two types of chlorine atoms.

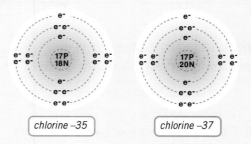

a) In what way are these atoms different? (2 marks)

....

....

b) What do we call these different forms of the same element? (1 mark)

....

....

c) What is a radioisotope? (1 mark)

....

....

4 a) What is an ion? (1 mark)

....

....

b) Explain why alpha particles are better ionisers than beta particles. (2 marks)

....

....

....

Radioactive decay

A

1 **Which statement about atoms undergoing radioactive decay is true?** (1 mark)

a) They undergo radioactive decay in order to become more stable. ☐

b) They undergo radioactive decay more quickly at high temperatures. ☐

c) They undergo radioactive decay more quickly at low temperatures. ☐

d) They undergo radioactive decay during a chemical reaction. ☐

2 **What is the amount of radiation emitted each second known as?** (1 mark)

a) the half-life of the source ☐

b) the radiation level ☐

c) the rate of reaction ☐

d) the activity of the source ☐

3 **A radioactive source contains 64 million undecayed nuclei. After 12 days, it contains 8 million undecayed nuclei. What is the half-life of the source?** (1 mark)

a) 6 days ☐
b) 2 days ☐
c) 4 days ☐
d) 3 days ☐

4 **The activity of a radioisotope is 400 disintegrations per second. If the half-life of the isotope is 2 hours, calculate its activity after 8 hours.** (1 mark)

a) 100 disintegrations per second ☐

b) 50 disintegrations per second ☐

c) 200 disintegrations per second ☐

d) 25 disintegrations per second ☐

5 **What does the emission of gamma radiation from a nucleus reduce?** (1 mark)

a) the atomic weight of the nucleus ☐

b) the mass of the nucleus ☐

c) the charge on the nucleus ☐

d) the energy in the nucleus ☐

B

1 Complete the following radioactive decay equations.

a) $^{226}_{88}\text{Ra}$ $\rightarrow$ $^{222}_{86}\text{Rn}$ + $^{x}_{y}\text{?}$ (3 marks)

unstable radium nucleus   more stable radon nucleus

b) $^{14}_{6}\text{C}$ $\rightarrow$ $^{14}_{7}\text{N}$ + $^{p}_{q}\text{?}$ (3 marks)

unstable carbon nucleus   more stable nitrogen nucleus

c) $^{238}_{92}\text{U}$ $\rightarrow$ $^{r}_{s}\text{?}$ + $^{4}_{2}\text{He}$ (3 marks)

unstable uranium nucleus   emitted alpha particle

d) $^{90}_{38}\text{Sr}$ $\rightarrow$ $^{u}_{v}\text{?}$ + $^{0}_{-1}\text{e}$ (3 marks)

unstable strontium nucleus   emitted beta particle

C

1 a) Explain what is meant by the phrase 'the activity of a radioactive source'. **(2 marks)**

....

....

b) Explain what is meant by the sentence 'the half-life of radon-222 is 4 days'. **(3 marks)**

....

....

....

c) A radioisotope contains 64×10^{10} undecayed nuclei. After 12 days, it contains 4×10^{10} undecayed nuclei. Calculate the half-life of the isotope. **(3 marks)**

....

....

....

d) How many undecayed nuclei will remain in the above source after a further 6 days? **(2 marks)**

....

....

2 The table below shows how the activity of a radioisotope changed with time.

Activity/counts per minute	Time/hours
240	0
152	2
101	4
62	6
40	8
25	10
15	12
12	14
6	16

a) Plot a graph to show how the activity of the source changed with time. **(5 marks)**

b) Use the graph to determine the half-life of the radioisotope. **(3 marks)**

....

....

c) Calculate the activity of the source after 18 hours. **(2 marks)**

....

....

Uses of radioactivity

A

1 **What is produced by the alpha emitter inside a smoke detector?** (1 mark)

a) atoms ☐
b) ions ☐
c) protons ☐
d) neutrons ☐

2 **In which of these situations would a radioactive tracer not be used?** (1 mark)

a) sterilisation of food ☐
b) to monitor the flow of blood in the body ☐
c) to check for leaks in a gas pipe ☐
d) to check the progress of food through the digestive system ☐

3 **Which of the following combinations could be used to monitor the thickness of a material produced as a sheet?** (1 mark)

a) gamma radiation to monitor the thickness of paper ☐
b) alpha radiation to monitor the thickness of card ☐
c) beta radiation to monitor the thickness of paper ☐
d) alpha radiation to monitor the thickness of steel ☐

4 **A narrow beam of radiation can be used to kill cancerous cells. What is this treatment called?** (1 mark)

a) radiotherapy ☐
b) radioactivity ☐
c) sterilisation ☐
d) radioscopy ☐

5 **Which of the following might be exposed to gamma radiation in order to kill bacteria?** (1 mark)

a) antiseptic ☐
b) a surgeon's hands ☐
c) disinfectant ☐
d) surgical instruments ☐

B

1 **The diagram shows a smoke detector.**

A description of how the smoke detector works is given below, but parts of it have been omitted. Fill in the missing words. (9 marks)

The smoke detector contains a radioisotope that emits **a)** .... These collide with

b) .... creating **c)** .... As a result, a **d)** .... flows. If

e) .... enters the detector, fewer **f)** .... are produced, so the **g)** ....

becomes **h)** .... and the alarm **i)** ....

2 **a)** **What causes food to rot?** (1 mark)

....

b) **Explain how radioactivity can be used so that foods keep for much longer.** (2 marks)

....

C

1 The diagram below shows how a radioactive source is used in radiotherapy.

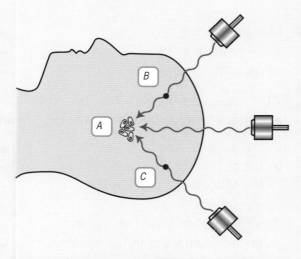

a) Name the type of radioactivity emitted by the source. (1 mark)

....

....

b) What happens to the cancerous cells at A? (2 marks)

....

....

....

c) Why does this not happen to cells at B or C? (1 mark)

....

....

....

....

2 The diagram below shows a man using a radiation detector.

The fluid in the pipe has been labelled with a gamma emitter.

a) Suggest one material that might be flowing through the pipe. (1 mark)

....

b) What is the man trying to find? (1 mark)

....

....

c) How will he know when he finds it? (1 mark)

....

d) Why is the fluid not labelled with an alpha or beta emitter? (1 mark)

....

....

e) Give one advantage of this technique. (2 marks)

....

....

How well did you do? ✗ 0-7 **Try again** 8-15 **Getting there** 16-21 **Good work** 22-27 **Excellent!** ✓

Nuclear power

A

1 **Which of the following describes nuclear fusion?** (1 mark)

a) the joining of small nuclei to make heavier nuclei ☐
b) takes place in a nuclear power station ☐
c) takes place on the Moon ☐
d) is the splitting of large nuclei into smaller nuclei ☐

2 **Which of the following describes nuclear fission?** (1 mark)

a) is taking place in all stars ☐
b) is the joining of two light nuclei of roughly equal mass ☐
c) is taking place on the Sun ☐
d) is the splitting of a heavy nucleus into two lighter nuclei of roughly equal mass ☐

3 **What is the process of dismantling and disposing of an old nuclear reactor called?** (1 mark)

a) degrading ☐

b) dispositioning ☐
c) decomposing ☐
d) decommissioning ☐

4 **What causes the uranium-235 in a nuclear reactor to become unstable?** (1 mark)

a) the nucleus absorbing a proton ☐
b) the nucleus absorbing a neutron ☐
c) the temperature of the reactor increasing ☐
d) a chemical reaction between the uranium and water in the reactor ☐

5 **The control rods in a nuclear reactor:** (1 mark)

a) are made from uranium-235 ☐
b) control the flow of water into and out of the reactor ☐
c) absorb neutrons ☐
d) can speed up the rate of the nuclear reaction by pushing them further into the reactor vessel ☐

B

1 **The diagram below shows the main parts of a nuclear power station.**

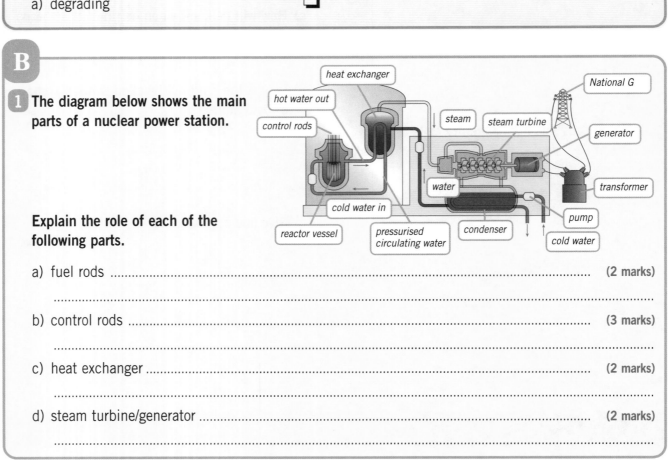

Explain the role of each of the following parts.

a) fuel rods .... (2 marks)

....

b) control rods .... (3 marks)

....

c) heat exchanger .... (2 marks)

....

d) steam turbine/generator .... (2 marks)

....

C

1 The equation below describes a nuclear fusion reaction.

$$^2_1H + {}^2_1H \xrightarrow{\text{fusion reaction}} {}^3_2H + {}^1_0n + \text{Energy}$$

a) Explain the phrase 'nuclear fusion reaction'. (2 marks)

....

b) Why does a nuclear fusion reaction take place? (1 mark)

....

c) Give one example of a situation in which nuclear fusion reactions are continuously taking place. (1 mark)

....

2 The equation below describes a nuclear fission reaction.

$$^{235}_{92}U + {}^1_0n \longrightarrow {}^{141}_{56}Ba + {}^{92}_{36}Kr + 3{}^1_0n + \text{Energy}$$

a) Explain the phrase 'nuclear fission reaction'. (2 marks)

....

The above reaction may take place in a nuclear reactor.

b) Explain why this reaction, if uncontrolled, could lead to a nuclear explosion. (2 marks)

....

....

c) Explain how the reaction is controlled in a nuclear reactor. (4 marks)

....

....

....

d) Explain why the decommissioning of a nuclear reactor is very expensive and hazardous. (2 marks)

....

Notes